S0-BDP-578

**Houghton
Mifflin
Harcourt**

© Houghton Mifflin Harcourt Publishing Company • Cover Image Credits: (Bighorn Sheep)©Blaine Harrington III/
Alamy Images; (Watchman Peak, Utah) ©Russ Bishop/Alamy Images

Copyright © 2015 by Houghton Mifflin Harcourt Publishing Company

All rights reserved. No part of this work may be reproduced or transmitted in any form or by any means, electronic or mechanical, including photocopying or recording, or by any information storage and retrieval system, without the prior written permission of the copyright owner unless such copying is expressly permitted by federal copyright law. Requests for permission to make copies of any part of the work should be addressed to Houghton Mifflin Harcourt Publishing Company, Attn: Contracts, Copyrights, and Licensing, 9400 Southpark Center Loop, Orlando, Florida 32819-8647.

Common Core State Standards © Copyright 2010. National Governors Association Center for Best Practices and Council of Chief State School Officers. All rights reserved.

This product is not sponsored or endorsed by the Common Core State Standards Initiative of the National Governors Association Center for Best Practices and the Council of Chief State School Officers.

Printed in the U.S.A.

ISBN 978-0-544-29322-9

3 4 5 6 7 8 9 10 1678 22 21 20 19 18 17 16 15
4500529900   B C D E F G

If you have received these materials as examination copies free of charge, Houghton Mifflin Harcourt Publishing Company retains title to the materials and they may not be resold. Resale of examination copies is strictly prohibited.

Possession of this publication in print format does not entitle users to convert this publication, or any portion of it, into electronic format.

Critical Area Ratios and Rates

 Common Core **CRITICAL AREA** Connecting ratio and rate to whole number multiplication and division and using concepts of ratio and rate to solve problems

Lessons   **Grade 6 Common Core State Standards**

Domain: Ratios and Proportional Relationships   **6.RP**

6.1–6.5   Cluster A: **Understand ratio concepts and use ratio reasoning to solve problems.**
       6.RP.A.3   Use ratio and rate reasoning to solve real-world and mathematical problems, e.g., by reasoning about tables of equivalent ratios, tape diagrams, double number line diagrams, or equations.

d. Use ratio reasoning to convert measurement units; manipulate and transform units appropriately when multiplying or dividing quantities.

Table of Contents

Chapter 6 Units of Measure

Domain:
Ratios and Proportional Relationships   6.RP

Common Core MATHEMATICAL PRACTICES

MP1 Make sense of problems and persevere in solving them.

MP2 Reason abstractly and quantitatively.

MP3 Construct viable arguments and critique the reasoning of others.

MP4 Model with mathematics.

MP5 Use appropriate tools strategically.

MP6 Attend to precision.

MP7 Look for and make use of structure.

MP8 Look for and express regularity in repeated reasoning.

Chapter At A Glance

Domain: Ratios and Proportional Relationships

Chapter Essential Question How can you use measurements to help you describe and compare objects?

Use the *Go Math! Planning Guide* for correlation, math practice information, and more.

Lesson At A Glance

	1 Day LESSON 6.1 `Common Core` 6.RP.A.3d	**1 Day** LESSON 6.2 `Common Core` 6.RP.A.3d	**1 Day** LESSON 6.3 `Common Core` 6.RP.A.3d
	Convert Units of Length 315A	**Convert Units of Capacity** 321A	**Convert Units of Weight and Mass** 327A
Essential Question	How can you use ratio reasoning to convert from one unit of length to another?	How can you use ratio reasoning to convert from one unit of capacity to another?	How can you use ratio reasoning to convert from one unit of weight or mass to another?
Objective	Use ratio reasoning to convert from one unit of length to another.	Use ratio reasoning to convert from one unit of capacity to another.	Use ratio reasoning to convert from one unit of weight or mass to another.
Vocabulary	**conversion factor,** length, meter	**capacity,** gallon, liter, pint, quart	gram, mass, ounce, pound, ton, weight
ELL Strategy	**ELL** Strategy • Develop Meanings	**ELL** Strategy • Identify Relationships	**ELL** Strategy • Rephrase

Go online to access all your chapter resources

www.thinkcentral.com

6.1 *i*Student Edition	6.2 *i*Student Edition	6.3 *i*Student Edition
6.1 *e*Teacher Edition	6.2 *e*Teacher Edition	6.3 *e*Teacher Edition
Personal Math Trainer	Personal Math Trainer	Personal Math Trainer
Math on the Spot Video	Math on the Spot Video	Math on the Spot Video
*i*T *i*Tools	*i*T *i*Tools	*i*T *i*Tools
HMH Mega Math	HMH Mega Math	HMH Mega Math

Print Resources

6.1 Student Edition	6.2 Student Edition	6.3 Student Edition
6.1 Practice and Homework (in the *Student Edition*)	6.2 Practice and Homework (in the *Student Edition*)	6.3 Practice and Homework (in the *Student Edition*)
6.1 Reteach (in the *Chapter Resources*)	6.2 Reteach (in the *Chapter Resources*)	6.3 Reteach (in the *Chapter Resources*)
6.1 Enrich (in the *Chapter Resources*)	6.2 Enrich (in the *Chapter Resources*)	6.3 Enrich (in the *Chapter Resources*)
Grab-and-Go™ Centers Kit	Grab-and-Go™ Centers Kit	Grab-and-Go™ Centers Kit

Response to Intervention

Before the Chapter	**During the Lesson**	**After the Chapter**
✓ **Show What You Know**	✓ **Share and Show**	✓ **Chapter Review/Test**
• Prerequisite Skills Activities	• Reteach	• Reteach
• Personal Math Trainer	• Mid-Chapter Checkpoint	• Personal Math Trainer
	• Personal Math Trainer	• Reteach Activity (online)
	• Reteach Activity (online)	

1 Day

LESSON 6.4 6.RP.A.3d

Transform Units 335A

How can you transform units to solve problems?

Transform units to solve problems.

ELL Strategy • Identify Relationships

1-2 Days

LESSON 6.5 6.RP.A.3d

Problem Solving • Distance, Rate, and Time Formulas. 341A

How can you use the strategy *use a formula* to solve problems involving distance, rate, and time?

Solve problems involving distance, rate, and time by applying the strategy *use a formula*.

ELL Strategy • Identify Relationships

Teacher Notes

6.4 *i*Student Edition
6.4 *e*Teacher Edition
Personal Math Trainer
Math on the Spot Video
*i*T *i*Tools

6.5 *i*Student Edition
6.5 *e*Teacher Edition
Personal Math Trainer
Math on the Spot Video
✔ Chapter 6 Test
Real World Video, Ch. 6
Animated Math Models

6.4 Student Edition
6.4 Practice and Homework (in the *Student Edition*)
6.4 Reteach (in the *Chapter Resources*)
6.4 Enrich (in the *Chapter Resources*)
Grab-and-Go™ Centers Kit

6.5 Student Edition
6.5 Practice and Homework (in the *Student Edition*)
6.5 Reteach (in the *Chapter Resources*)
6.5 Enrich (in the *Chapter Resources*)
Grab-and-Go™ Centers Kit

 GO DIGITAL

Resources *www.thinkcentral.com*

 Interactive Student Edition
 Personal Math Trainer
 Math on the Spot Video
Animated Math Models
 Assessment
MM HMH Mega Math
 *i*Tools
Multimedia *e*Glossary
 Professional Development Videos
 Real World Videos

PROFESSIONAL DEVELOPMENT

Teaching for Depth

Steven J. Leinwand
Principal Research Analyst
American Institutes for Research (AIR)
Washington, D.C.

Making Sense of Conversions

Students frequently are not sure whether to multiply or divide when they need to convert from one unit of measure to another. They should think about the relationship of the units. These questions, based on the relationship of the units, will help students determine the operation they should use.

- How are the units related—what is the relationship or formula?

- Is the unit being converted smaller or larger than the target unit?

To illustrate these questions, convert within the U.S. monetary system, which should be familiar to all students.

- How many dimes are in 23 dollars?

- How many dollars are in 35 dimes?

Encourage discussion and establish the formulas relating the units:

$$1 \text{ dollar} = 10 \text{ dimes}$$
$$1 \text{ dime} = \frac{1}{10} \text{ or } 0.1 \text{ dollar}$$

Guide students to conclude that when you start with a coin of greater value and convert to a denomination of less value, the result will be a greater number and vice versa. The focus must be on reasoning rather than on determining whether to divide or multiply.

From the Research

"Mathematically proficient students ... continuously ask themselves, "Does this make sense?"" (NGA Center/CCSSO, 2010, p. 6)

Converting to Other Systems

Benchmarks such as 1 inch is about 2.5 centimeters may be close enough to help students understand some measures. However, other situations require more accuracy. For example, an inch is equal to 2.54 centimeters. So, to find the number of centimeters in 4 inches, begin with the relationship of inches to centimeters.

$$1 \text{ inch} = 2.54 \text{ centimeters}$$
$$4 \text{ inches} = 4 \times 2.54 \text{ centimeters}$$

By thinking about the relationship first, it becomes clear to the student whether to multiply or divide.

Common Core Mathematical Practices

Mathematically proficient students **make sense of problems and persevere in solving them.** Sense making requires:

- Understanding what is given and what is asked

- Looking for a logical path to the solution by recalling formulas and related problems, not by performing mindless computations

- Computing to arrive at a solution

- Checking that the solution makes sense

- Justifying the solution with reasonable arguments

Many students attempt to solve problems before reflecting on relationships and procedures previously acquired that apply to the present problem. The sense making process requires patience and leads to success in mathematics.

Daily Classroom Management

Differentiated Instruction

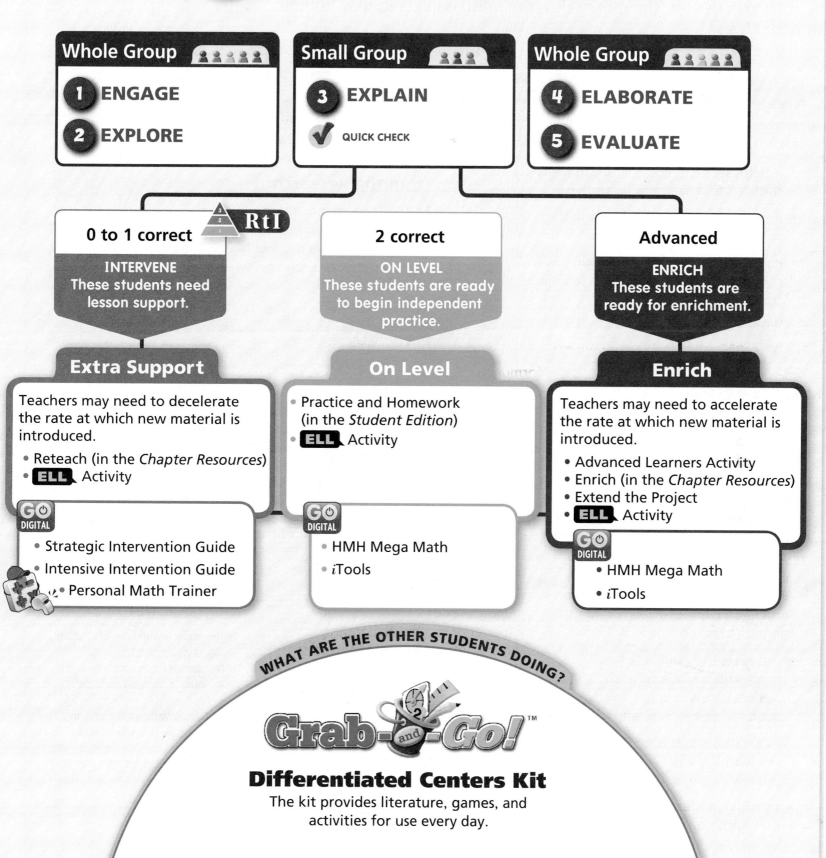

Whole Group	Small Group	Whole Group
1 ENGAGE	**3 EXPLAIN**	**4 ELABORATE**
2 EXPLORE	✓ QUICK CHECK	**5 EVALUATE**

0 to 1 correct — RtI

INTERVENE
These students need lesson support.

2 correct

ON LEVEL
These students are ready to begin independent practice.

Advanced

ENRICH
These students are ready for enrichment.

Extra Support

Teachers may need to decelerate the rate at which new material is introduced.

- Reteach (in the *Chapter Resources*)
- **ELL** Activity

GO DIGITAL

- Strategic Intervention Guide
- Intensive Intervention Guide
- Personal Math Trainer

On Level

- Practice and Homework (in the *Student Edition*)
- **ELL** Activity

GO DIGITAL

- HMH Mega Math
- *i*Tools

Enrich

Teachers may need to accelerate the rate at which new material is introduced.

- Advanced Learners Activity
- Enrich (in the *Chapter Resources*)
- Extend the Project
- **ELL** Activity

GO DIGITAL

- HMH Mega Math
- *i*Tools

WHAT ARE THE OTHER STUDENTS DOING?

Grab-and-Go!™

Differentiated Centers Kit
The kit provides literature, games, and activities for use every day.

Strategies for
English Language Learners

The *Identify Relationships Strategy* makes connections between new concepts and something familiar. The more connections made to students' experiences, the more relevance math is likely to play in their minds and lives.

by Elizabeth Jiménez
CEO, GEMAS Consulting
Professional Expert on
English Learner Education
Bilingual Education and Dual Language
Pomona, California

Benefit to English Language Learners

When introducing new concepts, teachers must look for ways to identify relationships. The Identify Relationships strategy is beneficial to English Language Learners because:

- it helps students consider math concepts in contexts that are familiar to them.

- it makes it easier to understand the structure of a math problem.

- it reduces anxiety by introducing new concepts in relationship with familiar concepts.

From the Research

"Knowledge about the linguistic and cultural practices in students' communities is essential if teachers are to make connections between the content they are trying to teach and what their students already know."

Trumbull, E., Nelson-Barber, S., & Mitchell, J. (2002). *Enhancing mathematics instruction for indigenous American students.* In J. Hankes & G. Fast (Eds.), *Changing the faces of mathematics: Perspectives of indigenous people of North America (pp. 1-18).* Reston, VA: NCTM.

Planning for Instruction

Identifying relationships in mathematics involves building new understanding from previous experiences and understanding connections between math topics. Teachers should look for ways to connect new information to previous learning and to the prior knowledge of the students.

Anchoring the essential framework for a math concept to what English Language Learners already know:

- increases the number of connections students make between new and previously acquired knowledge and language,

- helps students bridge what they are learning with what they already know, and

- provides students the foundation on which new learning can build.

Taking the time to connect to students' prior knowledge and experience can be challenging when students struggle to express themselves because they are still learning English. However, doing so allows you to separate language from content knowledge. Some English Language Learners may have already learned the math concepts and simply need to acquire the language to express that knowledge. Only by taking time do you know which students need which emphasis.

Linguistic Note

When working with units of measure, students will encounter many abbreviations for the common units of measure. If English Language Learners have lived outside the U.S., they may know the metric system rather than the customary system. Take advantage of that expertise, but remember that the abbreviations may change from language to language.

Developing Math Language

Chapter Vocabulary

capacity the amount that a container can hold

conversion factor a rate in which the two quantities are equal, but use different units

mass the amount of matter an object has

weight the measure of how heavy an object is

 Visualize It
Have students list the metric units of capacity from largest to smallest in this graphic organizer to show the relative sizes of the units.

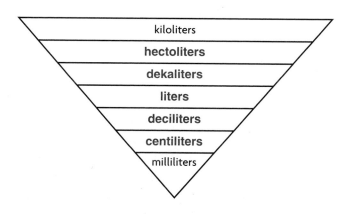

| kiloliters |
| hectoliters |
| dekaliters |
| liters |
| deciliters |
| centiliters |
| milliliters |

GO DIGITAL
• Interactive Student Edition
• Multimedia eGlossary

ELL Vocabulary Activity

See ELL Activity Guide for leveled activities.

Objective Develop and use vocabulary from the metric and customary systems of measurement.

Materials index cards

Have students write the customary and metric units of measurement on index cards. Shuffle the cards, and have students work together to stack the cards by the types of measure in each system (i.e., length, capacity, weight/mass). Then have students sort the cards in each stack from the smallest unit to largest unit. Ask students to describe the equivalencies among measures. For example, there are 12 *inches* in 1 *foot*.

Practice vocabulary by using questioning strategies such as:

Beginning
• What does a deciliter measure?

Intermediate
• Which is larger, a hectometer or a dekameter?

Advanced
• Which number is greater: the number of grams that represents the mass of a book or the number of decigrams that represents the mass of the same book? Explain.

Vocabulary Strategy • Graphic Organizer

Materials Word Line (see *eTeacher Resources*)

Word Line Have students write the word *gram* in the center rectangle of a word line.

List the metric prefixes on the board: *centi-, deci-, milli-, deka-, hecto-,* and *kilo-*.

Have students fill in the ovals with the prefixes in order from largest (on the left) to smallest (on the right).

Review Prerequisite Skills

RtI Activities

TIER 2

Analyze It!

Objective Use patterns to multiply and divide by powers of 10.

Students can use patterns to help them multiply and divide by powers of 10.
Present these number sentences to students.

$1,458 \div 10 = 145.8$	$0.34 \times 10 = 3.4$
$1,458 \div 100 = 14.58$	$0.34 \times 100 = 34$
$1,458 \div 1,000 = 1.458$	$0.34 \times 1,000 = 340$

Have students look at the placement of the decimal point in each quotient. Ask students to describe the patterns they see. Possible answer: The decimal point in

1,458 moves to the left the same number of places as the number of zeros in the power of 10.

Have students look at the placement of the decimal point in each product, and ask them to describe the patterns they see. Possible answer: The decimal point in 0.34 moves to the right the same number of places as the number of zeros in the power of 10.

Explain to students that understanding how to use patterns to multiply and divide by powers of 10 will help them convert metric measurements.

TIER 3

Draw It!

Objective Identify benchmarks for metric and customary units.
Materials poster board, color pencils

It is important for students to understand the relative size of customary and metric units. Common objects can serve as benchmark measurements.

Tell students that a slice of bread weighs about 1 ounce. Ask them to think of other objects that might weigh about 1 ounce. Possible answers: an eraser, a CD, 20 index cards

Have students write *ounce* on their posters and draw several objects that weigh about 1 ounce.

Repeat with other common units, such as an inch (diameter of a quarter), meter (width of a door), centimeter (width of a fingernail), pound (weight of pair of athletic shoes), kilogram (mass of a baseball bat), gram (mass of a paper clip), gallon (capacity of a milk jug), and liter (capacity of a water bottle).

Have students label each unit on their posters with its system (customary or metric) and type (length, capacity, weight, or mass).

Ratios and Proportional Relationships

Common Core Learning Progressions Across the Grades

In Grade 5, students

- convert like measurement units within a given measurement system.

In Grade 6, students will

- use relationships given by unit rates to convert measurement units
- use equations to represent proportional relationships.

In Grade 7, students will

- use graphing to decide if two quantities are proportional.

Common Core State Standards Across the Grades

Before

Domain: Measurement and Data
Convert like measurement units within a given measurement system.
5.MD.A.1

Grade 6

Domain: Ratios and Proportional Relationships
Understand ratio concepts and use ratio reasoning to solve problems.
6.RP.A.3d

After

Domain: Ratios and Proportional Relationships
Analyze proportional relationships and use them to solve real-world and mathematical problems.
7.RP.A.1

See A page of each lesson for Common Core Standard text.

Chapter 6

Introduce the Chapter

Assessing Prior Knowledge

Use **Show What You Know** to determine if students need intensive or strategic intervention.

In this problem, students need to transform units in order to solve a problem. They will learn about transforming units in Lesson 6.4.

- **How many yards are equivalent to 1 mile?** 1,760 yards

- **What is the cheetah's rate in miles per hour?** 60 miles per hour

- **How many minutes are in 1 hour?** 60 minutes

Chapter 6 Units of Measure

Show What You Know

Check your understanding of important skills.

Name _____

▶ **Choose the Appropriate Unit** Circle the more reasonable unit to measure the object. (4.MD.A.1)

1. the length of a car
   inches or **feet**

2. the length of a soccer field
   meters or kilometers

▶ **Multiply and Divide by 10, 100, and 1,000** Use mental math. (5.NBT.A.2)

3. 2.51×10
   25.1

4. 5.3×100
   530

5. $0.71 \times 1,000$
   710

6. $3.25 \div 10$
   0.325

7. $8.65 \div 100$
   0.0865

8. $56.2 \div 1,000$
   0.0562

▶ **Convert Units** Complete. (5.MD.A.1)

9. $12\ lb = \blacksquare\ oz$
   Think: 1 lb = 16 oz
   192 oz

10. $8\ c = \blacksquare\ pt$
    Think: 2 c = 1 pt
    4 pt

11. $84\ in. = \blacksquare\ ft$
    Think: 12 in. = 1 ft
    7 ft

A cheetah can run at a rate of 105,600 yards per hour. Find the number of miles the cheetah could run at this rate in 5 minutes. 5 miles

Chapter 6   313

© Houghton Mifflin Harcourt Publishing Company • Image Credits: (b) ©DLILLC/Corbis

---

✓ Show What You Know • Diagnostic Assessment

Use to determine if students need intervention for the chapter's prerequisite skills.

Were students successful with Show What You Know?

| If NO...then **INTERVENE** | If YES...then use **INDEPENDENT ACTIVITIES** |

	Skill	Missed More Than	Personal Math Trainer	Intervene With
TIER 3	Choose the Appropriate Unit	0	4.MD.A.1	*Intensive Intervention* Skill 53; *Intensive Intervention User Guide* Activity 6
TIER 2	Multiply and Divide by 10, 100, and 1,000	2	5.NBT.A.2	*Strategic Intervention* Skill 11
TIER 2	Convert Units	1	5.MD.A.1	*Strategic Intervention* Skill 33

Differentiated Centers Kit

Use the Enrich Activity in the *Chapter Resources* or the independent activities in the *Grab-and-Go™ Differentiated Centers Kit.*

Vocabulary Builder

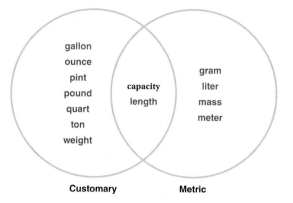

▶ **Visualize It**

Sort the review words into the Venn diagram.

gallon
ounce
pint
pound
quart
ton
weight

capacity
length

gram
liter
mass
meter

Customary   **Metric**

Review Words

✓ gallon
  gram
✓ length
  liter
✓ mass
  meter
  ounce
  pint
  pound
✓ quart
  ton
✓ weight

Preview Words

✓ capacity
✓ conversion factor

▶ **Understand Vocabulary**

Complete the sentences by using the checked words.

1. A rate in which the two quantities are equal but use different
   units is called a ___conversion factor___.

2. ___Mass___ is the the amount of matter in an object.

3. ___Capacity___ is the amount a container can hold.

4. The ___weight___ of an object tells how heavy the object is.

5. Inches, feet, and yards are all customary units used to measure
   ___length___.

6. A ___gallon___ is a larger unit of capacity than a quart.

• Interactive Student Edition
• Multimedia eGlossary

© Houghton Mifflin Harcourt Publishing Company

314

Vocabulary Builder

Have students complete the activities on this page by working alone or with partners.

▶ **Visualize It**

A Venn diagram shows relationships among sets. Students should write the words related to customary measurement in the left circle and the words related to metric measurement in the right circle. The words that are used in both systems, such as *capacity* and *length,* should be written in the intersection of the circles.

▶ **Understand Vocabulary**

Introduce the new words for the chapter.

Students can enhance their understanding of key chapter vocabulary through the use of the vocabulary cards found in the Student Edition. Have students cut out the cards and create their own deck of terms. You can use these cards to reinforce knowledge and reading across the content areas.

School-Home Letter available in English and Spanish in the Chapter Resources. Multiple languages available online at *www.thinkcentral.com.*

Intervention Options 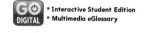 **RtI** Response to Intervention

Use Show What You Know, Lesson Quick Check, and Assessments to diagnose students' intervention levels.

TIER 1	**TIER 2**	**TIER 3**	**ENRICHMENT**
On-Level Intervention	**Strategic Intervention**	**Intensive Intervention**	**Independent Activities**
For students who are generally at grade level but need early intervention with the lesson concepts, use:	For students who need small group instruction to review concepts and skills needed for the chapter, use:	For students who need one-on-one instruction to build foundational skills for the chapter, use:	For students who successfully complete lessons, use:

TIER 1 — On-Level Intervention

- **Reteach** (in the *Chapter Resources*)
- **Personal Math Trainer**
- ▲ **Tier 1 Activity** online

TIER 2 — Strategic Intervention

- **Strategic Intervention Guide**
- **Personal Math Trainer**
- **Prerequisite Skills Activities**
- **Tier 2 Activity** online

TIER 3 — Intensive Intervention

- **Intensive Intervention Guide**
- **Personal Math Trainer**
- **Prerequisite Skills Activities**

ENRICHMENT — Independent Activities

Differentiated Centers Kit

- **Advanced Learners Activity** for every lesson
- **Enrich Activity** (in the *Chapter Resources*)

 HMH Mega Math

Units of Measure 314

Going Places with GO Math Words

Introduce the Words

Provide these student-friendly explanations for the vocabulary from this chapter.

- The *capacity* of a container is the amount it can hold.
- 36 is a *common factor* of 6 and 12 because it is a factor of both numbers.
- $\frac{1 \text{ yard}}{3 \text{ feet}}$ is a *conversion factor* because the quantities 1 yard and 3 feet have different units but are equal in value.
- A *square unit* is a unit of area that has the dimensions of 1 unit by 1 unit.
- An object's *weight* tells how heavy it is.

Math Journal ┃WRITE ▸Math

Have students draw pictures or use numbers to show what each term means. Then ask them to discuss their work with a partner.

Bingo:

Play the Game

The game may be played before, during, or after the content is taught. Read the game directions with students. Divide students into groups, and have each group choose a student to be the caller. Explain that the caller chooses a Vocabulary Card, reads the definition, and then puts the card in a second pile. Have each group play until a player marks 5 boxes in a row going down, across, or diagonally and calls "Bingo." Ask the caller to check the definitions read as the winner reads the words.

The directions for playing the game can also be found in the Chapter Resource book.

ELL Discuss any game terms to ensure that students understand their meanings.

Bingo

For 3–6 players

Materials
- 1 set of word cards
- 1 Bingo board for each player
- game markers

How to Play
1. The caller chooses a card and reads the definition. Then the caller puts the card in a second pile.
2. Players put a marker on the word that matches the definition each time they find it on their Bingo boards.
3. Repeat Steps 1 and 2 until a player marks 5 boxes in a line going down, across, or on a slant and calls "Bingo."
4. To check the answers, the player who said "Bingo" reads the words aloud while the caller checks the definitions.

Word Box
capacity
common factor
conversion factor
denominator
formula
numerator
square unit
weight

Chapter 6   314A

Journal

The Write Way

Reflect

Choose one idea. Write about it.

- Describe a situation in which you might use a conversion factor.
- Sumeer has a jar that holds 4 cups of water. Eliza has a bottle that holds 3 pints of water. Explain whose container has the greater capacity.
- If the area of a room is 20 feet by 6 yards, tell how to figure out the room's area in square feet.
- Write and solve a word problem that uses the formula $d = r \times t$.

© Houghton Mifflin Harcourt Publishing Company   Image Credits: ©David Madison/Stone/Getty Images

314B

What You Need

Each group of players needs one copy of the following Vocabulary Cards on *eTeacher Resources* pp. **TR114–TR133**: *capacity, common factor, conversion factor*. Use index cards to make Vocabulary Cards for *denominator, formula, numerator, square unit, weight,* and other additional words. You may also wish to create your own sets of cards.

Each player needs one copy of the Bingo board on *eTeacher Resources* p. **TR145** and about 10–15 game markers. Have each player write the vocabulary words from this chapter in random order in all the boxes on the Bingo board. Point out that they may write each word more than once.

The Write Way

These short, informal writing activities address the vocabulary and content from this chapter. Communicating about math clarifies and deepens students' understandings about math concepts.

Read the writing prompts with students. Give them 5–10 minutes to choose an idea and write about it.

When students have completed their first drafts, share and discuss the following questions. Then provide students with additional time to use the questions to review and revise their writing.

- **Does my writing show that I understand the math idea(s)?**
- **Do I use math vocabulary correctly?**
- **Is my writing clear and easy to follow?**
- **Do I use complete sentences? Have I checked to be sure my grammar, spelling, and punctuation are correct?**

Ask volunteers to share their finished writing with a partner or the class. Encourage discussion of different ways students may have addressed each prompt. Point out that often there is not just one correct answer.

ELL Have students use the Vocabulary Cards in the Student Edition as a reference for word meanings. Guide them to use the lessons and example problems in the Student Edition if they need additional support.

Convert Units of Length

LESSON AT A GLANCE

FOCUS **COHERENCE** **RIGOR**

F C R Focus:

Common Core State Standards

6.RP.A.3d Use ratio and rate reasoning to solve real-world and mathematical problems, e.g., by reasoning about tables of equivalent ratios, tape diagrams, double number line diagrams, or equations. Use ratio reasoning to convert measurement units; manipulate and transform units appropriately when multiplying or dividing quantities.

MATHEMATICAL PRACTICES
MP1 Make sense of problems and persevere in solving them.
MP2 Reason abstractly and quantitatively. **MP6** Attend to precision.

F C R Coherence:

Standards Across the Grades
Before   **Grade 6**   **After**
5.MD.A.1   6.RP.A.3d   7.RP.A.1

F C R Rigor:

Level 1: Understand Concepts....................*Share and Show* (✓ Checked Items)
Level 2: Procedural Skills and Fluency........*On Your Own*
Level 3: Applications.................................*Think Smarter and Go Deeper*

Learning Objective
Use ratio reasoning to convert from one unit of length to another.

Language Objective
Student pairs describe a real-world example to explain the use of ratio reasoning to convert from one unit of length to another.

Materials
MathBoard

F C R For more about how *GO Math!* fosters **Coherence** within the Content Standards and Mathematical Progressions for this chapter, see page 313H.

About the Math

Professional Development

Using a Metric Conversion Chart

Rather than using conversion factors to convert metric units of measurement, students can use the conversion chart shown here. The chart is simple to use because the metric system is based on powers of 10. For each space that you move, you either multiply or divide by 10. For example, if you move left three spaces, you are dividing by 10 × 10 × 10, or 1,000. Lead students through the following activity.

- Use the chart to convert 354 centimeters to hectometers. Place your pencil point on the space that shows "centi-."

- To move to the space labeled "hecto-," you must move left four spaces. This means you are dividing by 10,000.

- The number of spaces that you move tells you how many places to move the decimal point. Move the decimal point to the left 4 places.

- Therefore, 354 cm = 0.0354 hm.

 Professional Development Videos

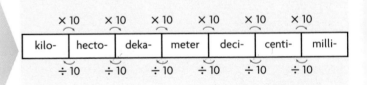

Daily Routines
Common Core

 Problem of the Day 6.1
Alisha spent $5.84 on 8 oranges and $4.26 on 6 apples. What is the unit cost for each orange? $0.73

Vocabulary conversion factor

 • Interactive Student Edition
• Multimedia eGlossary

Fluency Builder | Common Core Fluency Standard 6.NS.B.3

Materials eTeacher Resources page TR138

Decimal Multiplication Have students multiply whole numbers and decimals.

1. 502×6.2 3,112.4

2. 4.6×18 82.8

3. 108.2×0.5 54.1

4. 80.64×3.25 262.08

5. 203.8×0.05 10.19

6. 18.02×36.5 657.73

$$5.84 \div 8 = \$.73$$

❶ ENGAGE

with the Interactive Student Edition

Essential Question
How can you use ratio reasoning to convert from one unit of length to another?

Making Connections
Review units of measure with students.

• **What are the two measurement systems we use?** customary and metric

• **What are some units of length?** customary: inch, foot, yard, mile; metric: centimeter, meter, kilometer

Learning Activity
What is the problem the students are trying to solve? Connect the story to the problem.

• Coco's family is going to run a 5-kilometer race. What unit do they want to convert that distance into? meters.

• **When else might you want to convert units of length?** Sample: Instructions for building something are given in one unit, and your ruler uses a different unit.

Literacy and Mathematics
View the lesson opener with the students. Then, complete the following activity:

• **Have students write a story about a real-life situation in which they would need to convert units of length.**

② EXPLORE

Guide students through the first paragraph.

- **What is a factor?** a number that is multiplied by another number

- A *conversion factor* is a rate that is used to **convert a measurement from one unit to another. What is a rate?** a ratio that compares two quantities with different units

MP6 Attend to precision. How is a quantity different from a number? A quantity is a measurement that uses a number, such as 6 feet or 2 goals.

Unlock the Problem

Common Core MATHEMATICAL PRACTICES

- **You need to convert 33 feet to yards. Which is larger: feet or yards?** yards **Since you are converting to a larger unit, it takes fewer of them to make 33 feet.**

Explain how to simplify the common units when converting feet to yards.

- **Remember: You can divide the numerators and denominators of fractions by a common factor without changing the value. What unit of measure appears in both a numerator and a denominator?** feet **Divide the numerator and denominator by feet, and you are left with just yards in the numerator.**

MP2 Reason abstractly and quantitatively.

Direct students' attention to the next problem.

- **You need to convert from feet to inches. Do you expect more inches than feet? Or fewer inches than feet? Explain.** Since inches are smaller than feet, I expect more inches than feet.

 Math Talk Use **Math Talk** to focus on students' understanding of how to choose conversion factors that will yield an answer with the desired units.

ELL Strategy:
Develop Meanings

Explain that an abbreviation is a shorter way of writing a word or phrase.

- Write on index cards abbreviations for customary and metric units of length. Help students write the term for the abbreviation on the back to each card.

- Use a ruler and yardstick to model how to measure length in customary and metric units of length.

6.RP.A.3d Use ratio and rate reasoning to solve real-world and mathematical problems, e.g., by reasoning about tables of equivalent ratios, tape diagrams, double number line diagrams, or equations. Use ratio reasoning to convert measurement units; manipulate and transform units appropriately when multiplying or dividing quantities.

Name _____

Lesson **6.1**

Convert Units of Length

Essential Question How can you use ratio reasoning to convert from one unit of length to another?

 Ratios and Proportional Relationships—6.RP.A.3d
MATHEMATICAL PRACTICES
MP2, MP6, MP8

In the customary measurement system, some of the common units of length are inches, feet, yards, and miles. You can multiply by an appropriate conversion factor to convert between units. A **conversion factor** is a rate in which the two quantities are equal, but use different units.

Customary Units of Length

1 foot (ft) = 12 inches (in.)
1 yard (yd) = 36 inches
1 yard = 3 feet
1 mile (mi) = 5,280 feet
1 mile = 1,760 yards

Unlock the Problem

In a soccer game, Kyle scored a goal. Kyle was 33 feet from the goal. How many yards from the goal was he?

Math Idea
When the same unit appears in a numerator and a denominator, you can divide by the common unit before multiplying as you would with a common factor.

Convert 33 feet to yards.

Choose a conversion factor. **Think:** I'm converting *to* yards *from* feet.

1 yard = 3 feet, so use the rate $\frac{1 \text{ yd}}{3 \text{ ft}}$.

Multiply 33 feet by the conversion factor. Units of *feet* appear in a numerator and a denominator, so you can divide the units before multiplying.

$33 \text{ ft} \times \frac{1 \text{ yd}}{3 \text{ ft}} = \frac{33 \text{ ft}}{1} \times \frac{1 \text{ yd}}{3 \text{ ft}} = \underline{11} \text{ yd}$

So, Kyle was __11__ yards from the goal.

How many inches from the goal was Kyle?

Choose a conversion factor. **Think:** I'm converting *to* inches *from* feet.

12 inches = 1 foot, so use the rate $\frac{12 \text{ in.}}{1 \text{ ft}}$.

Multiply 33 ft by the conversion factor.

$33 \text{ ft} \times \frac{12 \text{ in.}}{1 \text{ ft}} = \frac{33 \text{ ft}}{1} \times \frac{12 \text{ in.}}{1 \text{ ft}} = \underline{396} \text{ in.}$

So, Kyle was __396__ inches from the goal.

Possible explanation: Use the units you are converting to in the numerator and the units you want to convert from in the denominator, so the common units will simplify to 1.

Math Talk MATHEMATICAL PRACTICES ⑥
Explain How do you know which unit to use in the numerator and which unit to use in the denominator of a conversion factor?

Chapter 6 **315**

Reteach 6.1 ▲ **RtI**

Name _____
Lesson 6.1
Reteach

Convert Units of Length

To convert a unit of measure, multiply by a conversion factor. A **conversion factor** is a rate in which the two quantities are equal, but are expressed in different units.

Convert to the given unit. 2,112 ft = ___ mi

Customary Units of Length
1 foot (ft) = 12 inches (in.)
1 yard (yd) = 36 inches
1 yard = 3 feet
1 mile = 5,280 feet
1 mile = 1,760 yards

Step 1 Choose a conversion factor.

1 mile = 5,280 feet, so use the conversion factor $\frac{1 \text{ mi}}{5,280 \text{ ft}}$

Step 2 Multiply by the conversion factor.

$2,112 \text{ ft} \times \frac{1 \text{ mi}}{5,280 \text{ ft}} = \frac{2,112 \text{ ft}}{1} \times \frac{1 \text{ mi}}{5,280 \text{ ft}} = \frac{2}{5} \text{ mi}$

So, 2,112 ft = $\frac{2}{5}$ mi.

When converting metric units, move the decimal point to multiply or divide by a power of ten.

14 dm = ___ hm

| kilo- | hecto- | deka- | meter | deci- | centi- | milli- |

Step 1 Start at the given unit.

Step 2 Move to the unit you are converting to.

Step 3 Move the decimal point that same number of spaces in the same direction. Fill any empty place-value positions with zeros.

So, 14 dm = 0.014 hm.

Convert to the given unit.

1. 4.5 miles = __7,920__ yards
2. 0.8 hectometers = __80,000__ millimeters
3. 48 inches = __4__ feet
4. 45 centimeters = __0.045__ dekameters

Chapter Resources
© Houghton Mifflin Harcourt Publishing Company
6-5
Reteach

Enrich 6.1 **Differentiated Instruction**

Name _____
Lesson 6.1
Enrich

Lotta Giga Nano

The metric system has linear units that are larger than a kilometer. The metric system also has linear units that are smaller than a millimeter. Some of them are given in the table below.

	×1,000		×1,000		×1,000		×1,000		×1,000		×1,000	
gigameter (Gm)		megameter (Mm)		kilometer (km)		meter (m)		millimeter (mm)		micrometer (µm)		nanometer (nm)
	÷1,000		÷1,000		÷1,000		÷1,000		÷1,000		÷1,000	

To convert from one unit to the next, multiply or divide by 1,000.

Write *multiply* or *divide*. Decide how many times to multiply or divide by 1,000 to convert to the given unit. Then find the value.

1. 24 Mm = ■ m
multiply; 2 times;
24,000,000

2. 458 µm = ■ m
divide; 2 times;
0.000458

3. 5 km = ■ m
multiply; 1 time;
5,000

4. 8 nm = ■ m
divide; 3 times;
0.000000008

5. 971 Gm = ■ m
multiply; 3 times;
971,000,000,000

6. 12 nm = ■ mm
divide; 2 times;
0.000012

7. 38 mm = ■ km
divide; 2 times;
0.000038

8. 7 Gm = ■ Mm
multiply; 1 time;
7,000

9. 795 nm = ■ Mm
divide; 5 times;
0.000000000000795

10. 156 km = ■ mm
multiply; 1 time;
156,000

Chapter Resources
© Houghton Mifflin Harcourt Publishing Company
6-6
Enrich

Metric Units You can use a similar process to convert metric units. Metric units are used throughout most of the world. One advantage of using the metric system is that the units are related by powers of 10.

Metric Units of Length
1,000 millimeters (mm) = 1 meter (m)
100 centimeters (cm) = 1 meter
10 decimeters (dm) = 1 meter
1 dekameter (dam) = 10 meters
1 hectometer (hm) = 100 meters
1 kilometer (km) = 1,000 meters

 Example A passenger airplane is 73.9 meters long. What is the length of the airplane in centimeters? What is the length in kilometers?

⚠ ERROR Alert
Be sure to use the correct conversion factor. The units you are converting from should simplify to 1, leaving only the units you are converting to.

 One Way Use a conversion factor.

73.9 meters = ■ centimeters

Choose a conversion factor. 100 cm = 1 m, so use the rate $\frac{100 \text{ cm}}{1 \text{ m}}$.

Multiply 73.9 meters by the conversion factor. Simplify the common units before multiplying.

$$\frac{73.9 \cancel{m}}{1} \times \frac{100 \text{ cm}}{1 \cancel{m}} = 7{,}390 \text{ cm}$$

So, 73.9 meters is equal to __7,390__ centimeters.

 Another Way Use powers of 10.

Metric units are related to each other by factors of 10.

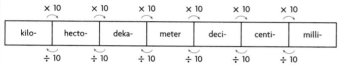

| kilo- | hecto- | deka- | meter | deci- | centi- | milli- |

73.9 meters = ■ kilometers

Use the chart.

Kilometers are 3 places to the left of meters in the chart. Move the decimal point 3 places to the left. This is the same as dividing by 1,000.

73.9   0.0739

So, 73.9 meters is equal to __0.0739__ kilometer.

The number of decimeters will be less than the number of centimeters because you will divide by 10 to find the number of decimeters.

 MATHEMATICAL PRACTICES ②

Reasoning If you convert 285 centimeters to decimeters, will the number of decimeters be greater or less than the number of centimeters? Explain.

316

© Houghton Mifflin Harcourt Publishing Company

Metric Units Have students look at the table of metric equivalencies.

- **Why might working with metric units be easier than working with customary units?** Metric units are based on powers of 10. So you end up multiplying or dividing by a power of 10 when converting units, which means you can just move the decimal point.

One Way

- **In this problem, we are converting meters to centimeters. How are these units related?** 100 centimeters = 1 meter

- **Centimeters are much smaller than meters. Will the number of centimeters be less than or greater than 73.9?** greater than **How do you know?** Since centimeters are smaller than meters, it will take many more centimeters to cover the distance of 73.9 meters.

Another Way

- **How can you check your answer?** Convert 0.0739 kilometer to meters. There are 1,000 meters in a kilometer, so we need to multiply by 1,000. This is the same as moving the decimal point three places to the right. 0.0739 km = 73.9 m

 Use **Math Talk** to focus on students' understanding of how to convert metric units of length. Students may not be familiar with decimeters, but they can use the conversion table to compare sizes. Ask students how many millimeters equal 1 decimeter. 100 millimeters

---

Advanced Learners
Visual, Kinesthetic
Whole Class / Small Group

Materials rulers, tape measures

- Have students use a ruler to measure the length of the room in feet. Answers will vary.

- Then, have students convert the measurement to inches by using a conversion factor. Check students' work.

- Next, have students use the tape measure to find the length of the room in inches. Answers will vary.

- Ask students to compare the two measurements in inches.

- Are your measurements exactly the same? Explain. Possible answer: no; Measurements obtained with different tools can vary slightly. All measurements are approximate.

⚠ COMMON ERRORS

Error When converting metric measurements, students might count an initial decimal place when moving the decimal point, thereby moving one place too few.

Example 73.9 m = 0.739 km

Springboard to Learning Have students place their pencil points on the decimal point in 73.9. Explain that they start counting only after they have moved one place. Consider having students draw arrows that indicate the movement to each place until they have improved their accuracy.

Lesson 6.1   316

3 EXPLAIN

Share and Show

The first problem connects to the learning model. Have students use the MathBoard to explain their thinking.

Use the checked exercises for **Quick Check**. Students should show their answers for the Quick Check on the MathBoard.

 Quick Check

 a student misses the checked exercises

 Differentiate Instruction with
- Reteach 6.1
- Personal Math Trainer 6.RP.A.3d
- RtI Tier 1 Activity (online)

Math Talk Use **Math Talk** to focus on students' understanding of how to convert inches to yards. Have students recall the number of inches in a foot, and the number of inches in a yard.

On Your Own
- **In Exercise 8, will you move the decimal point to the left or to the right? How do you know?** to the left; Possible explanation: Hectometers are to the left of meters in the conversion chart.

GO DEEPER In Exercise 9 call students' attention to the fact that the problem requires that they change not only feet to yards, but also minutes to half hours.

Name _____

Share and Show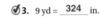

Convert to the given unit.

1. 3 miles = ■ yards

   conversion factor: $\dfrac{1,760 \text{ yd}}{1 \text{ mi}}$

   3 miles = $\dfrac{3 \text{ mi}}{1} \times \dfrac{1,760 \text{ yd}}{1 \text{ mi}}$ = __5,280__ yd

2. 43 dm = __0.043__ hm

☑ 3. 9 yd = __324__ in.

4. 72 ft = __24__ yd

☑ 5. 7,500 mm = __75__ dm

Possible answer: To convert from inches to yards, multiply the number of inches by $\frac{1 \text{ yd}}{36 \text{ in.}}$. To convert from yards to inches, multiply the number of yards by $\frac{36 \text{ in.}}{1 \text{ yd}}$.

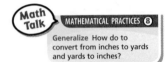

Math Talk **MATHEMATICAL PRACTICES ❽**
Generalize How do to convert from inches to yards and yards to inches?

On Your Own

6. Rohan used 9 yards of ribbon to wrap gifts. How many inches of ribbon did he use?

   __324 in.__

7. One species of frog can grow to a maximum length of 12.4 millimeters. What is the maximum length of this frog species in centimeters?

   __1.24 cm__

8. The height of the Empire State Building measured to the top of the lightning rod is approximately 443.1 meters. What is this height in hectometers?

   __4.431 hm__

9. **GO DEEPER** A snail moves at a speed of 2.5 feet per minute. How many yards will the snail have moved in half of an hour?

   __25 yd__

Practice: Copy and Solve Compare. Write <, >, or =.

10. 32 feet ⊘< 11 yards

11. 537 cm ＝ 5.37 m

12. 75 inches ＞ 6 feet

© Houghton Mifflin Harcourt Publishing Company

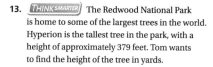

Problem Solving • Applications

What's the Error?

13. **THINK SMARTER** The Redwood National Park is home to some of the largest trees in the world. Hyperion is the tallest tree in the park, with a height of approximately 379 feet. Tom wants to find the height of the tree in yards.

Tom converted the height this way:

$$3 \text{ feet} = 1 \text{ yard}$$

conversion factor: $\frac{3 \text{ ft}}{1 \text{ yd}}$

$$\frac{379 \text{ ft}}{1} \times \frac{3 \text{ ft}}{1 \text{ yd}} = 1,137 \text{ yd}$$

Find and describe Tom's error.	**Show how to correctly convert from 379 feet to yards.**
Tom did not use the correct conversion factor, so the common units will not simplify.	conversion factor: $\frac{1 \text{ yd}}{3 \text{ ft}}$ $\frac{379 \cancel{\text{ft}}}{1} \times \frac{1 \text{ yd}}{3 \cancel{\text{ft}}} = 126\frac{1}{3} \text{ yd}$

So, 379 feet = $126\frac{1}{3}$ yards.

- **MATHEMATICAL PRACTICE 6** Explain how you knew Tom's answer was incorrect.

  Possible answer: Since yards are larger units than feet, the tree must be less than 379 yards tall and Tom's answer of 1,137 yards must be wrong.

14. **THINK SMARTER** Choose <, >, or =.

14a. 12 yards [< > =] 432 inches

14b. 321 cm [< > =] 32.1 m

318

DIFFERENTIATED INSTRUCTION   INDEPENDENT ACTIVITIES

Differentiated Centers Kit

Activities
Estimating Units of Measure

Students complete online orange Activity Card 17 by choosing the appropriate unit of measure for different objects.

Literature
A Peek into a Tiny World

Students read about using a stage micrometer to make measurements of tiny creatures.

© Houghton Mifflin Harcourt Publishing Company • Image Credits: (r) ©Vito Palmisano/Getty Images

4 ELABORATE

Problem Solving • Applications

Common Core **MATHEMATICAL PRACTICES**

THINK SMARTER

What's the Error? Have students read Exercise 13.

- **Is it true that there are 3 feet in 1 yard?** yes **Did Tom use the conversion factor correctly? Explain.** No; he needs to set up the problem so that the common units, feet, simplify to 1, leaving yards in the numerator.

MP6 Attend to precision. Students may point out that the units can't cancel because of the way the conversion factor is written or recognize that the number of yards should be less than the number of feet.

Math on the Spot Video Tutor

Use this video to help students model and solve this type of *Think Smarter* problem.

GO DIGITAL **Math on the Spot** videos are in the Interactive Student Edition and at *www.thinkcentral.com*.

THINK SMARTER

Exercise 14 assesses a student's ability to use <, >, or = to compare units of length. Students who incorrectly answer this item may not have used the correct conversion factor. It is important for students to make the connection that a conversion factor is a rate in which two quantities are equal, but use different units.

5 EVALUATE Formative Assessment

Essential Question
Using the Language Objective

Reflect Have students work in pairs to describe a real-world example to answer the Essential Question.

How can you use ratio reasoning to convert from one unit of length to another? Find a conversion factor that relates the given unit and the needed unit. Multiply the given amount by the conversion factor, and be sure that the conversion factor is written so that the common units will simplify.

Math Journal WRITE ▸ *Math*

Explain why units can be simplified first when measurements are multiplied.

Practice and Homework

Use the Practice and Homework pages to provide students with more practice of the concepts and skills presented in this lesson. Students master their understanding as they complete practice items and then challenge their critical thinking skills with Problem Solving. Use the Write Math section to determine student's understanding of content for this lesson. Encourage students to use their Math Journals to record their answers.

Name _____

Convert Units of Length

COMMON CORE STANDARD—6.RP.A.3d
Understand ratio concepts and use ratio reasoning to solve problems.

Convert to the given unit.

1. 42 ft = ☐ yd

conversion factor: $\frac{1 \text{ yd}}{3 \text{ ft}}$

42 ft × $\frac{1 \text{ yd}}{3 \text{ ft}}$

42 ft = 14 yd

2. 2,350 m = ☐ km

_____2.35_____

3. 18 ft = ☐ in.

_____216_____

4. 289 m = ☐ dm

_____2,890_____

5. 5 mi = ☐ yd

_____8,800_____

6. 35 mm = ☐ cm

_____3.5_____

Compare. Write <, >, or =.

7. 1.9 dm ⬭< 1,900 mm

8. 12 ft ⬭= 4 yd

9. 56 cm ⬭< 56,000 km

10. 98 in. ⬭> 8 ft

11. 64 cm ⬭> 630 mm

12. 2 mi ⬭= 10,560 ft

Problem Solving (Real World)

13. The giant swallowtail is the largest butterfly in the United States. Its wingspan can be as large as 16 centimeters. What is the maximum wingspan in millimeters?

_____160 mm_____

14. The 102nd floor of the Sears Tower in Chicago is the highest occupied floor. It is 1,431 feet above the ground. How many yards above the ground is the 102nd floor?

_____477 yd_____

15. **WRITE** ▸Math Explain why units can be simplified first when measurements are multiplied.

Possible explanation: When the same unit appears in a numerator and a denominator, you can simplify the common unit to 1 before multiplying as you would with a common factor.

Chapter 6   319

© Houghton Mifflin Harcourt Publishing Company

Extend the Math | Activity

Missing Measurements

This activity will help students use the skills of finding elapsed time and converting length measurements simultaneously.

Investigate Have students refer to the conversion chart on page 315 to help them solve the problem.

- *Manuel walked a total distance of 8,523 ft from 4:18 P.M. to 4:50 P.M. Morgan walked a total distance of 1.24 mi from 1:48 P.M. to 2:10 P.M. Who walked at a faster average rate?* Manuel walked 8,523 ft in 32 min, or about 266.3 ft per min. Morgan walked 1.24 mi, or 6,547.2 ft, in 22 min, which equals 297.6 ft per min. So, Morgan walked at a faster rate.

Math Talk Use these questions to help students get started.

- **What are you asked to find?** who walked at the faster average rate
- **How can you find each person's average rate in feet per minute?** Divide feet by minutes for each person.
- **How can you find the number of feet Morgan walked?** Use the conversion factor relating feet and miles.
- **How can you find the number of minutes each person walked?** Find the elapsed time for each person.

Summarize Have students discuss why knowing how to work with measurements is important. Ask them to list all the skills they used to solve this word problem.

Lesson Check (6.RP.A.3d)

1. Justin rides his bicycle 2.5 kilometers to school. Luke walks 1,950 meters to school. How much farther does Justin ride to school than Luke walks to school?

2. The length of a room is $10\frac{1}{2}$ feet. What is the length of the room in inches?

____550 meters____

____126 inches____

Spiral Review (6.NS.C.8, 6.RP.A.3a, 6.RP.A.3c)

3. Each unit on the map represents 1 mile. What is the distance between the campground and the waterfall?

____4 miles____

4. On a field trip, 2 vans can carry 32 students. How many students can go on a field trip when there are 6 vans?

____96 students____

5. According to a 2008 survey, $\frac{29}{50}$ of all teens have sent at least one text message in their lives. What percent of teens have sent a text message?

____58%____

6. Of the students in Ms. Danver's class, 6 walk to school. This represents 30% of her students. How many students are in Ms. Danver's class?

____20 students____

© Houghton Mifflin Harcourt Publishing Company

FOR MORE PRACTICE
GO TO THE
Personal Math Trainer

Continue concepts and skills practice with Lesson Check. Use Spiral Review to engage students in previously taught concepts and to promote content retention. Common Core standards are correlated to each section.

Convert Units of Capacity

LESSON AT A GLANCE

FOCUS   COHERENCE   RIGOR

F C R Focus:

 Common Core State Standards

6.RP.A.3d Use ratio and rate reasoning to solve real-world and mathematical problems, e.g., by reasoning about tables of equivalent ratios, tape diagrams, double number line diagrams, or equations. Use ratio reasoning to convert measurement units; manipulate and transform units appropriately when multiplying or dividing quantities.

MATHEMATICAL PRACTICES

MP2 Reason abstractly and quantitatively.   **MP4** Model with mathematics.
MP8 Look for and express regularity in repeated reasoning.

F C R Coherence:

Standards Across the Grades

Before	Grade 6	After
5.MD.A.1	6.RP.A.3d	7.RP.A.1

F C R Rigor:

Level 1: Understand Concepts....................*Share and Show* (✓ Checked Items)
Level 2: Procedural Skills and Fluency.......*On Your Own*
Level 3: Applications...............................*Think Smarter and Go Deeper*

Learning Objective

Use ratio reasoning to convert from one unit of capacity to another.

Language Objective

Students write on their MathBoard to show a partner how you can use ratio reasoning to convert from one unit of capacity to another.

Materials

MathBoard

F C R For more about how *GO Math!* fosters **Coherence** within the Content Standards and Mathematical Progressions for this chapter, see page 313H.

About the Math
Professional Development

Why Teach This

It is important that students learn about the customary system of measurement, the system used in the United States, as well as the metric system of measurement, the system used in most other countries.

- To have a sense of the magnitude of measurements, students should learn the relationships among different measures and how to convert from one measurement unit to another.

- Moving the decimal point to convert metric units reinforces that the system is based on powers of 10. It gives students practice with multiplying and dividing by powers of 10. Converting customary units reinforces students' understanding of rates and equivalent rates.

 Professional Development Videos

 DIGITAL

 Interactive Student Edition

 Personal Math Trainer

 Math on the Spot

 *i*Tools: Measurement

 HMH Mega Math

Daily Routines

Common Core

 Problem of the Day 6.2

Marshall wants to know how many inches there are in 7 feet. Which conversion factor should Marshall use? $\frac{12 \text{ inches}}{1 \text{ foot}}$

Vocabulary capacity

 • Interactive Student Edition
• Multimedia eGlossary

Vocabulary Builder

Semantic Feature Analysis Have pairs of students complete the table.

	1 fl oz	1 c	1 qt
It is larger than a bowl of soup.	false	false	true
It is smaller than a pint.	true	true	false
It is a metric unit of measure.	false	false	false

Literature Connection

From the Grab-and-Go™ Differentiated Centers Kit

Students read about using a stage micrometer to make measurements of tiny creatures.

A Peek into a Tiny World

① ENGAGE

with the Interactive Student Edition

Essential Question

How can you use ratio reasoning to convert from one unit of capacity to another?

Making Connections

Review units of capacity with students.

• **What are some units of capacity?** customary: cup, pint, quart, gallon; metric: milliliter, liter

Learning Activity

What is the problem the students are trying to solve? Connect the story to the problem.

• **How many gallons of water does the fish tank hold?** 9 gallons

• **What type of measuring container does Mr. Nettles have?** a 1-pint measuring container

• **What are you trying to find?** the number of times Mr. Nettles needs to fill the 1-pint container to equal 9 gallons

Literacy and Mathematics

View the lesson opener with the students. Then, complete the following activity:

• Have students write a story about planning a party. Their stories should include a shopping list that has at least three items that are measured in units of capacity.

2 EXPLORE

Unlock the Problem

Have students read the first paragraph and look at the equivalencies in the table.

Explain to students that *fluid ounces* are different from *ounces*—fluid ounces measure volume, but ounces measure weight.

- **What common items are sold in gallons?**
  Possible answers: milk, gasoline, water

MP2 Reason abstractly and quantitatively. Direct students' attention to the conversion of 25 quarts to gallons.

- **Which is larger—a quart or a gallon?** gallon
  When changing from quarts to gallons, why will your answer be less than 25?
  Gallons are larger, so it takes fewer of them.

Direct students' attention to the conversion of 25 quarts to pints.

- **How do you know that the number of pints will be greater than the number of quarts?**
  A pint is a smaller unit than a quart.

Explain that to find the number of pints, students should write a rate with pints in the numerator and quarts in the denominator.

MP2 Reason abstractly and quantitatively.

- **Would there be more cups or more fluid ounces in 25 quarts of milk? Explain.** There would be more fluid ounces because they are smaller than cups, so it would take more of them.

MP6 Attend to precision. Have students write the conversion factor for converting quarts to cups. Compare this to the conversion factor for converting cups to quarts.
$\frac{4 \text{ cups}}{1 \text{ quarts}}$; that conversion factor would use the same amounts, but the numerator and denominator would be exchanged.

 Strategy:

Identify Relationships

Show students containers of various sizes, and explain that each one has a different capacity, or amount the container can hold when filled.

- Use measuring cups to show the amount in an ounce, a cup, pint, quart, and gallon.

- Find yogurt, milk, juice, and ice cream in a newspaper ad. Ask, What is the capacity of this container?

6.RP.A.3d Use ratio and rate reasoning to solve real-world and mathematical problems, e.g., by reasoning about tables of equivalent ratios, tape diagrams, double number line diagrams, or equations. Use ratio reasoning to convert measurement units; manipulate and transform units appropriately when multiplying or dividing quantities.

Name _____

Lesson 6.2

Convert Units of Capacity

Essential Question How can you use ratio reasoning to convert from one unit of capacity to another?

 Ratios and Proportional Relationships—6.RP.A.3d
MATHEMATICAL PRACTICES
MP2, MP4, MP6, MP8

Capacity measures the amount a container can hold when filled. In the customary measurement system, some common units of capacity are fluid ounces, cups, pints, quarts, and gallons. You can convert between units by multiplying the given units by an appropriate conversion factor.

Customary Units of Capacity

8 fluid ounces (fl oz)	= 1 cup (c)
2 cups	= 1 pint (pt)
2 pints	= 1 quart (qt)
4 cups	= 1 quart
4 quarts	= 1 gallon (gal)

Unlock the Problem

A dairy cow produces about 25 quarts of milk each day. How many gallons of milk does the cow produce each day?

- How are quarts and gallons related?
  1 gal = 4 qt
- Why can you multiply a quantity by $\frac{1 \text{ gal}}{4 \text{ qt}}$ without changing the value of the quantity?
  Identity Property of Multiplication;
  1 gal = 4 qt, so $\frac{1 \text{ gal}}{4 \text{ qt}}$ equals 1.

Convert 25 quarts to gallons.

Choose a conversion factor. **Think:** I'm converting *to* gallons *from* quarts.

1 gallon = 4 quarts, so use the rate $\frac{1 \text{ gal}}{4 \text{ qt}}$.

Multiply 25 qt by the conversion factor.

$$25 \text{ qt} \times \frac{1 \text{ gal}}{4 \text{ qt}} = \frac{25 \text{ qt}}{1} \times \frac{1 \text{ gal}}{4 \text{ qt}} = 6\frac{1}{4} \text{ gal}$$

The fractional part of the answer can be renamed using the smaller unit.

$$6\frac{1}{4} \text{ gal} = \underline{6} \text{ gallons, } \underline{1} \text{ quart}$$

So, the cow produces ___6___ gallons, ___1___ quart of milk each day.

How many pints of milk does a cow produce each day?

Choose a conversion factor. **Think:** I'm converting *to* pints *from* quarts.

2 pints = 1 quart, so use the rate $\frac{2 \text{ pt}}{1 \text{ qt}}$.

Multiply 25 qt by the conversion factor.

$$25 \text{ qt} \times \frac{2 \text{ pt}}{1 \text{ qt}} = \frac{25 \text{ qt}}{1} \times \frac{2 \text{ pt}}{1 \text{ qt}} = \underline{50} \text{ pt}$$

So, the cow produces ___50___ pints of milk each day.

© Houghton Mifflin Harcourt Publishing Company

Reteach 6.2 RtI

Name _____

Lesson 6.2 Reteach

Convert Units of Capacity

Capacity is the measure of the amount that a container can hold. When converting customary units, multiply the initial measurement by a conversion factor.

Convert to the given unit. 35 c = ____ qt

Step 1 Choose a conversion factor.

1 quart = 4 cups, so use the conversion factor $\frac{1 \text{ quart}}{4 \text{ cups}}$.

Step 2 Multiply by the conversion factor.

$35 \text{ c} \times \frac{1 \text{ qt}}{4 \text{ c}} = \frac{35}{1} \times \frac{1 \text{ qt}}{4 \text{ c}} = \frac{35}{4} \text{ qt} = 8\frac{3}{4} \text{ qt}$

You can rename the fractional part using the smaller unit.

$8\frac{3}{4}$ quarts = 8 quarts, 3 cups

So, 35 c = $8\frac{3}{4}$ qt, or 8 qt, 3 c.

When converting metric units, move the decimal point to multiply or divide by a power of ten.

26 cL = ____ hL

kilo-	hecto-	deka-	liter	deci-	centi-	milli-

Step 1 Start at the given unit.

Step 2 Move to the unit you are converting to.

Step 3 Move the decimal point that same number of spaces in the same direction. Fill any empty place-value positions with zeros.

So, 26 cL = 0.0026 hL.

Convert to the given unit.

1. 0.72 kiloliters = __7,200__ deciliters
2. 78 qt = __19__ gal __2__ qt
3. 52 liters = __0.52__ hectoliters
4. 5 pints = __10__ cups

Customary Units of Capacity

8 fluid ounces (fl oz)	= 1 cup (c)
2 cups	= 1 pint (pt)
2 pints	= 1 quart (qt)
4 cups	= 1 quart
4 quarts	= 1 gallon (gal)

Enrich 6.2 **Differentiated Instruction**

Name _____

Lesson 6.2 Enrich

Mixed Up Capacity

The measurements in the first column were converted to other units with the results in the second column. However, the rows got mixed up. Connect each measurement in the first column with its conversion in the second column.

Original Measurements	Converted Measurements
2 gal	6 pt
89 mL	56 cups
8 pt	8 oz
3 qt	35 gal
8.9 L	500 daL
28 pints	500 dL
89 hL	0.0089 kL
113 cups	904 fl oz
140 qt	8.9 kL
5 kL	0.89 dL
0.5 hL	1 gal

1. Write Math Explain how you could convert 152 cups to gallons.

Possible answer: I can first convert 152 cups to 76 pints. Then I can convert 76 pints to 38 quarts. Finally, I can convert 38 quarts to $9\frac{1}{2}$ gallons.

Metric Units You can use a similar process to convert metric units of capacity. Just like metric units of length, metric units of capacity are related by powers of 10.

Metric Units of Capacity
1,000 milliliters (mL) = 1 liter (L)
100 centiliters (cL) = 1 liter
10 deciliters (dL) = 1 liter
1 dekaliter (daL) = 10 liters
1 hectoliter (hL) = 100 liters
1 kiloliter (kL) = 1,000 liters

Example A piece of Native American pottery has a capacity of 1.7 liters. What is the capacity of the pot in dekaliters? What is the capacity in milliliters?

One Way Use a conversion factor.

$$1.7 \text{ liters} = \blacksquare \text{ dekaliters}$$

Choose a conversion factor.

1 dekaliter = 10 liters, so use the rate
$$\frac{1 \text{ daL}}{10 \text{ L}}.$$

Multiply 1.7 L by the conversion factor.

$$\frac{1.7 \cancel{L}}{1} \times \frac{1 \text{ daL}}{10 \cancel{L}} = \underline{0.17} \text{ daL}$$

So, 1.7 liters is equivalent to $\underline{0.17}$ dekaliter.

Another Way Use powers of 10.

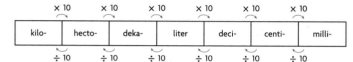

kilo-	hecto-	deka-	liter	deci-	centi-	milli-

× 10 (each step left to right) ÷ 10 (each step right to left)

$$1.7 \text{ liters} = \blacksquare \text{ milliliters}$$

Use the chart.

Milliliters are 3 places to the right of liters. So, move the decimal point 3 places to the right.

1.7   1700.

So, 1.7 liters is equal to $\underline{1,700}$ milliliters.

Possible explanation: In the customary system, unlike the metric system, units are not related to each other by powers of 10.

MATHEMATICAL PRACTICES ⑥

Explain Why can't you convert between units in the customary system by moving the decimal point left or right?

MATHEMATICAL PRACTICE ⑥ **Describe a Method** Describe how you would convert kiloliters to milliliters.

Possible answer: Multiply the number of kiloliters by 10^6, or 1,000,000.

322

© Houghton Mifflin Harcourt Publishing Company • Image Credits: ©American School/The Bridgeman Art Library/Getty Images

---

Example

Have students look at the metric conversion table at the top of the page. Point out that the prefixes in the chart are the same as those used to measure length.

One Way

- **How many liters are in 1 dekaliter?** 10 liters
  What is the conversion factor? $\frac{1 \text{ dekaliter}}{10 \text{ liters}}$

- **Multiplying 1.7 by $\frac{1}{10}$ is the same as dividing 1.7 by 10. What happens to the decimal point in 1.7 when you divide by 10?** It moves one place to the left.

Another Way

Direct students' attention to the conversion chart. **How can you use the conversion chart to convert measurements?** The conversion chart shows you how many places and in which direction to move the decimal point.

Math Talk Use **Math Talk** to focus on students' understanding of how to convert units within the metric system. **How can you use mental math to convert measurements in the metric system?** Moving the decimal point the correct number of places can be done using mental math.

MP6 Attend to precision. First have students determine the number of milliliters in one kiloliter. 1,000 mL = 1 L, 1,000 L = 1 kL

⚠ COMMON ERRORS

Error Students think that when converting from a smaller unit to a larger unit, the number of larger units will be greater than the number of smaller units because the unit is larger.

Example There are more than 25 gallons in 25 quarts because gallons are larger than quarts.

Springboard to Learning Ask a student to walk from one wall to another, and determine the number of steps. Then have the student take larger steps across the room, and compare the number of larger steps with the number of smaller steps. Point out that it takes fewer larger steps than smaller steps because the larger steps are longer than the smaller steps. Emphasize that it takes fewer larger units than smaller units to measure the same amount.

Advanced Learners 🕐 Visual, Kinesthetic / Partners / Small Group

Materials various unlabeled containers, rice or beans

- Provide a quart container, liter container, and gallon container for students, or have students bring them in.

- Ask students to predict how many liters are in a gallon. Then have students check their predictions by filling the liter container and pouring the contents into the gallon container. Students will need to express their answers in fraction or decimal form. about 3.8 liters

- Display the two statements: 1 L ≈ 1.06 qt and 1 qt ≈ 1.06 L. Explain that the ≈ symbol means "about equal to." Then have students use the containers and rice or beans to determine which statement correctly represents the relationship between liters and quarts. 1 L ⊕ 1.06 qt

3 EXPLAIN

Share and Show

The first problem connects to the learning model. Have students use the MathBoard to explain their thinking.

Use the checked exercises for **Quick Check**. Students should show their answers for the Quick Check on the MathBoard.

 Quick Check RtI

If ➤ a student misses the checked exercises

Then ➤ **Differentiate Instruction with**
- Reteach 6.2
- Personal Math Trainer 6.RP.A.3d
- RtI Tier 1 Activity (online)

On Your Own

MP2 Reason abstractly and quantitatively. For Exercise 8, elicit the fact from students that 1 deciliter of liquid is a smaller amount than 1 liter of liquid.

- **Direct attention to Exercises 10–15. How will you determine which symbol to use?** Convert one of the measurements so that they are both expressed in the same units. Then compare. Use the appropriate symbol to show the comparison.

 Use **Math Talk** to focus on students' understanding of how to convert units of capacity.

MP6 Attend to precision.

- **Compare the metric units of length and capacity. What do you notice?** Possible answer: They both use terms like milli, centi, and deci. Both are related by powers of 10.

Name _____

Convert to the given unit.

1. 5 quarts = ▪ cups

conversion factor: $\dfrac{4 \ c}{1 \ qt}$

5 quarts = $\dfrac{5 \ qt}{1} \times \dfrac{4 \ c}{1 \ qt}$ = __20__ c

2. 6.7 liters = __0.067__ hectoliters

☑ **3.** 5.3 kL = __5,300__ L

☑ **4.** 36 qt = __9__ gal

5. 5,000 mL = __500__ cL

Possible answer: the metric system; All conversion factors are powers of 10. In the customary system, conversion factors vary.

> **Math Talk**
> **MATHEMATICAL PRACTICES ⑥**
> Compare the customary and metric systems. In which system is it easier to convert from one unit to another?

On Your Own

6. It takes 41 gallons of water for a washing machine to wash a load of laundry. How many quarts of water does it take to wash one load?

_____164 qt_____

7. Sam squeezed 237 milliliters of juice from 4 oranges. How many liters of juice did Sam squeeze?

_____0.237 L_____

8. **MATHEMATICAL PRACTICE ②** Reason Quantitatively A bottle contains 3.78 liters of water. Without calculating, determine whether there are more or less than 3.78 deciliters of water in the bottle. Explain your reasoning.

There will be more than 3.78 dL

because 1 liter equals 10 dL.

9. **GO DEEPER** Tonya has a 1-quart, a 2-quart, and a 3-quart bowl. A recipe asks for 16 ounces of milk. If Tonya is going to triple the recipe, what is the smallest bowl that will hold the milk?

_____2-quart bowl_____

Practice: Copy and Solve Compare. Write <, >, or =.

10. 700,000 L ⊙> 70 kL

11. 6 gal ⊙< 30 qt

12. 54 kL ⊙= 540,000 dL

13. 10 pt ⊙= 5 qt

14. 500 mL ⊙< 50 L

15. 14 c ⊙< 4 qt

Chapter 6 • Lesson 2   323

Unlock the Problem

16. **THINK SMARTER** Jeffrey is loading cases of bottled water onto a freight elevator. There are 24 one-pint bottles in each case. The maximum weight that the elevator can carry is 1,000 pounds. If 1 gallon of water weighs 8.35 pounds, what is the maximum number of full cases Jeffrey can load onto the elevator?

a. What do you need to find?

the maximum number of cases of

24 one-pint water bottles whose total

weight is less than or equal to 1,000 lb

b. How can you find the weight of 1 case of bottled water? What is the weight?

Multiply the number of gallons that is

equivalent to 24 pints by 8.35; 25.05 lb

c. How can you find the number of cases that Jeffrey can load onto the elevator?

Divide 1,000 by 25.05, the weight of

one case. Since the answer must

be a whole number of cases with a

weight no more than 1,000 lb, round

the answer down to the nearest whole

number.

d. What is the maximum number of full cases Jeffrey can load onto the elevator?

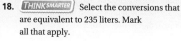
39 cases

17. **GO DEEPER** Monica put 1 liter, 1 deciliter, 1 centiliter, and 1 milliliter of water into a bowl. How many milliliters of water did she put in the bowl?

1,111 ml

18. **THINK SMARTER** Select the conversions that are equivalent to 235 liters. Mark all that apply.

- (A) 235,000 milliliters
- (B) 0.235 milliliters
- (C) 235,000 kiloliters
- (D) 0.235 kiloliters

© Houghton Mifflin Harcourt Publishing Company

 DIFFERENTIATED INSTRUCTION **INDEPENDENT ACTIVITIES**

Grab-and-Go!™
Differentiated Centers Kit

Activities
Estimating Units of Measure

Students complete online orange Activity Card 17 by choosing the appropriate unit of measure for different objects.

Literature
A Peek into a Tiny World

Students read about using a stage micrometer to make measurements of tiny creatures.

---

④ ELABORATE

Unlock the Problem

Common Core **MATHEMATICAL PRACTICES**

THINK SMARTER

- **What equivalency do you need to know to solve Problem 16?** how many pints are equal to 1 gallon

Math on the Spot Video Tutor

Use this video to help students model and solve this type of *Think Smarter* problem.

GO DIGITAL **Math on the Spot** videos are in the Interactive Student Edition and at *www.thinkcentral.com.*

THINK SMARTER

For Exercise 18, students must understand how to use ratio reasoning to convert from one metric unit of capacity to another. Students who incorrectly answer this item may not understand how to use powers of 10 to convert metric units of capacity. It is important for students to make the connection that just like metric units of length, metric units of capacity are related by powers of 10.

⑤ EVALUATE Formative Assessment

Essential Question
Using the Language Objective
Reflect Have student partners write on their MathBoard to answer the essential question.

How can you use ratio reasoning to convert from one unit of capacity to another?
Possible answer: Multiply the given capacity by a conversion factor. The numerator of the conversion factor should have the units you want to convert to. The denominator of the conversion factor should have the same units as the given capacity.

Math Journal **WRITE** ▸*Math*

Explain how units of length and capacity are similar in the metric system.

Practice and Homework

Use the Practice and Homework pages to provide students with more practice of the concepts and skills presented in this lesson. Students master their understanding as they complete practice items and then challenge their critical thinking skills with Problem Solving. Use the Write Math section to determine student's understanding of content for this lesson. Encourage students to use their Math Journals to record their answers.

Convert Units of Capacity

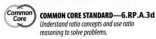

COMMON CORE STANDARD—6.RP.A.3d
Understand ratio concepts and use ratio reasoning to solve problems.

Convert to the given unit.

1. 7 gallons = [ ] quarts

   conversion factor: $\dfrac{4\ qt}{1\ gal}$

   7 gal × $\dfrac{4\ qt}{1\ gal}$

   7 gal = 28 qt

2. 5.1 liters = [ ] kiloliters

   Move the decimal point 3 places to the left.

   5.1 liters = 0.0051 kiloliters

3. 20 qt = [ ] gal

   _____ 5 _____

4. 40 L = [ ] mL

   _____ 40,000 _____

5. 33 pt = [ ] qt [ ] pt

   _____ 16; 1 _____

6. 29 cL = [ ] daL

   _____ 0.029 _____

7. 7.7 kL = [ ] cL

   _____ 770,000 _____

8. 24 fl oz = [ ] pt [ ] c

   _____ 1; 1 _____

Problem Solving (Real World)

9. A bottle contains 3.5 liters of water. A second bottle contains 3,750 milliliters of water. How many more milliliters are in the larger bottle than in the smaller bottle?

   _____ 250 mL _____

10. Arnie's car used 100 cups of gasoline during a drive. He paid $3.12 per gallon for gas. How much did the gas cost?

    _____ $19.50 _____

11. **WRITE** *Math* Explain how units of length and capacity are similar in the metric system.

    Check students' work.

    _____

    _____

© Houghton Mifflin Harcourt Publishing Company

Cross-Curricular   SCIENCE

- A science class is conducting a science experiment in which beakers of different solutions will be combined. The beakers contain different amounts of liquid. The teacher will combine all of the liquids into one large container.

- The beakers contain the following amounts: 0.3 liter, 26 milliliters, 4 centiliters, and 0.5 dekaliter. How many liters of solution will be poured into the large container? Convert each measurement to liters, and then add. 0.3 + 0.026 + 0.04 + 5 = 5.366 liters

SOCIAL STUDIES

- The table shows gas prices per gallon found in various U.S. cities in the winter of 2009. Determine the cost per cup for each city. Round to the nearest penny.
- Discuss why the prices per cup are so much closer to each other. The difference in price is less with small amounts, but as more and more gas is purchased, the difference increases.

City	Cost per Gallon	Cost per Cup
Baltimore, MD	$2.46	$0.15
Ashland, KS	$2.67	$0.17
Los Angeles, CA	$2.93	$0.18
Tallahassee, FL	$2.58	$0.16

325   Chapter 6

1. Gina filled a tub with 25 quarts of water. What is this amount in gallons and quarts?

2. Four horses are pulling a wagon. Each horse drinks 45,000 milliliters of water each day. How many liters of water will the horses drink in 5 days?

_____ 6 gallons, 1 quart _____

_____ 900 liters _____

Spiral Review (6.NS.C.8, 6.RP.A.2, 6.RP.A.3b, 6.RP.A.3c, 6.RP.A.3d)

3. The map shows Henry's town. Each unit represents 1 kilometer. After school, Henry walks to the library. How far does he walk?

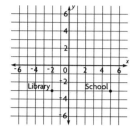

4. An elevator travels 117 feet in 6.5 seconds. What is the elevator's speed as a unit rate?

_____ 7 kilometers _____

_____ 18 feet per second _____

5. Julie's MP3 player contains 860 songs. If 20% of the songs are rap songs and 15% of the songs are R&B songs, how many of the songs are other types of songs?

6. How many kilometers are equivalent to 3,570 meters?

_____ 559 songs _____

_____ 3.57 kilometers _____

FOR MORE PRACTICE
GO TO THE
Personal Math Trainer

© Houghton Mifflin Harcourt Publishing Company

Continue concepts and skills practice with Lesson Check. Use Spiral Review to engage students in previously taught concepts and to promote content retention. Common Core standards are correlated to each section.

Convert Units of Weight and Mass

FOCUS COHERENCE RIGOR LESSON AT A GLANCE

F C R Focus:

Common Core State Standards

6.RP.A.3d Use ratio and rate reasoning to solve real-world and mathematical problems, e.g., by reasoning about tables of equivalent ratios, tape diagrams, double number line diagrams, or equations. Use ratio reasoning to convert measurement units; manipulate and transform units appropriately when multiplying or dividing quantities.

MATHEMATICAL PRACTICES
MP1 Make sense of problems and persevere in solving them. **MP2** Reason abstractly and quantitatively. **MP3** Construct viable arguments and critique the reasoning of others.

F C R Coherence:

Standards Across the Grades
Before **Grade 6** **After**
5.MD.A.1 6.RP.A.3d 7.RP.A.1

F C R Rigor:

Level 1: Understand Concepts....................*Share and Show* (✓ Checked Items)
Level 2: Procedural Skills and Fluency.......*On Your Own*
Level 3: Applications................................*Think Smarter and Go Deeper*

Learning Objective

Use ratio reasoning to convert from one unit of weight or mass to another.

Language Objective

Students work in teams to create a step-by-step information flier to show how you can use ratio reasoning to convert from one unit of weight or mass to another.

Materials

MathBoard

F C R For more about how *GO Math!* fosters **Coherence** within the Content Standards and Mathematical Progressions for this chapter, see page 313H.

About the Math
Professional Development

If Students Ask

Students may wonder what the difference is between weight and mass. Explain that *mass* is the amount of matter in an object, while *weight* is how heavy an object is.

Point out that because weight is the force that gravity exerts on an object, an object would weigh less on the moon than it does on Earth. However, since the amount of matter in the object does not change, its mass is the same in both places.

 Professional Development Videos

 SE Interactive Student Edition

 Personal Math Trainer

 Math on the Spot

 **iT** *iTools:* Measurement

 HMH Mega Math

Problem of the Day 6.3

Brian is unpacking boxes. He has been working for 3 hours and has already unpacked 9 boxes. At this rate, how long will it take him to unpack 15 boxes? 5 hours

 • Interactive Student Edition
• Multimedia eGlossary

3h → x
9b → 15

15 × 3 = 45

45 ÷ 9 = 5 hrs.

Fluency Builder

Common Core Fluency Standard 6.NS.B.3

Materials eTeacher Resources page TR138

Operations Have students multiply whole numbers and decimals.

1. $2.6 \times 52 =$ 135.2

2. $18 \times 3.05 =$ 54.9

3. $0.3 \times 1.8 =$ 0.54

4. $4.1 \times 7.5 =$ 30.75

5. $12.9 \times 0.75 =$ 9.675

1 ENGAGE

with the Interactive Student Edition

Essential Question

How can you use ratio reasoning to convert from one unit of weight or mass to another?

Making Connections

Have students name units of weight and mass.

- **What are some units of weight and mass?** customary: ounce, pound, ton; metric: milligram, gram, kilogram

Learning Activity

What is the problem the students are trying to solve? Connect the story to the problem.

- **What is the weight of the package Buddy's family member wants to mail at the post office?** 72 ounces

- **What are you trying to find?** the weight of the package in pounds

- **How many ounces are in 1 pound?** 16 ounces

Literacy and Mathematics

Ask students to describe how units of weight and mass are used in real-world contexts.

- Have students work in groups to create three real-world scenarios, each of which includes a different unit of weight or mass.

② **EXPLORE**

Materials *i*Tools: Measurement

Unlock the Problem

 MATHEMATICAL PRACTICES

- **Which is heavier: one pound or one ounce? Read the problem and complete the activity to learn how to convert customary units of weight.**

Direct students' attention to the conversion of 226 ounces to pounds.

- **Do you expect the number of pounds to be greater or less than 226? Why?** Possible answer: less; Pounds are larger than ounces, so fewer pounds are needed to measure the same weight.

- **Why is the remainder the smaller unit?** Possible answer: There aren't enough ounces to make another full pound, so there will be some ounces left over.

Direct students' attention to the conversion of 38 pounds to ounces.

MP6 Attend to precision.

- **How do you know what conversion factor to use?** The unit in the given measurement needs to match the unit in the denominator of the conversion factor so that the units will simplify to 1. Since the given measurement is in pounds, the denominator of the conversion factor needs to be pounds: $\frac{16 \text{ ounces}}{1 \text{ pound}}$.

Students may explore equivalent measures of weight by using *i*Tools: Measurement.

MP2 Reason abstractly and quantitatively.

- **Are there more ounces or pounds in 2 tons? Explain.** Possible answer: There are more ounces because ounces are smaller units than pounds.

MP4 Model with mathematics.

- **How could you find the weight of a 2-ton elephant in ounces?** Possible answer: Convert the 2 tons to pounds, then convert the pounds to ounces.

ELL **Strategy:**
Rephrase

Tell students that 1 ton = 2,000 lb.

- Ask students: **If an elephant weighs 8 tons, how many pounds does it weigh?** Have small groups use their own words to rewrite the question on a sheet of paper.

- Have small groups use words and illustrations to solve the problem on their paper. 16,000 pounds

---

6.RP.A.3d Use ratio and rate reasoning to solve real-world and mathematical problems, e.g., by reasoning about tables of equivalent ratios, tape diagrams, double number line diagrams, or equations. Use ratio reasoning to convert measurement units; manipulate and transform units appropriately when multiplying and dividing quantities.

Name _____

Lesson 6.3

Convert Units of Weight and Mass

Essential Question How can you use ratio reasoning to convert from one unit of weight or mass to another?

Common Core **Ratios and Proportional Relationships—6.RP.A.3d**
MATHEMATICAL PRACTICES
MP1, MP2, MP3, MP4

The weight of an object is a measure of how heavy it is. Units of weight in the customary measurement system include ounces, pounds, and tons.

Customary Units of Weight
1 pound (lb) = 16 ounces (oz)
1 ton (T) = 2,000 pounds

Unlock the Problem

The largest pearl ever found weighed 226 ounces. What was the pearl's weight in pounds?

- How are ounces and pounds related?
  1 lb = 16 oz
- Will you expect the number of pounds to be greater than 226 or less than 226? Explain.
  less than; every 16 oz is only 1 lb

🔑 **Convert 226 ounces to pounds.**

Choose a conversion factor.
Think: I'm converting *to* pounds *from* ounces.

1 lb = 16 oz, so use the rate $\frac{1}{16}\frac{\text{lb}}{\text{oz}}$.

Multiply 226 ounces by the conversion factor.

$$226 \text{ oz} \times \frac{1 \text{ lb}}{16 \text{ oz}} = \frac{226 \text{ oz}}{1} \times \frac{1 \text{ lb}}{16 \text{ oz}} = 14\frac{2}{16} \text{ lb}$$

Think: The fractional part of the answer can be renamed using the smaller unit.

$$14\frac{2}{16} \text{ lb} = \underline{14} \text{ lb}, \underline{2} \text{ oz}$$

So, the largest pearl weighed __14__ pounds, __2__ ounces.

🔑 **The largest emerald ever found weighed 38 pounds. What was its weight in ounces?**

Choose a conversion factor.
Think: I'm converting *to* ounces *from* pounds.

16 oz = 1 lb, so use the rate $\frac{16}{1}\frac{\text{oz}}{\text{lb}}$.

Multiply 38 lb by the conversion factor.

$$38 \text{ lb} \times \frac{16 \text{ oz}}{1 \text{ lb}} = \frac{38 \text{ lb}}{1} \times \frac{16 \text{ oz}}{1 \text{ lb}} = \underline{608} \text{ oz}$$

So, the emerald weighed __608__ ounces.

1. 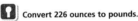 Model Mathematics Explain how you could convert the emerald's weight to tons.

Multiply 38 lb by $\frac{1 \text{ T}}{2,000 \text{ lb}}$.

Chapter 6 327

© Houghton Mifflin Harcourt Publishing Company • Image Credits: (b) ©Bon Appetit/Alamy

---

Differentiated Instruction

Reteach 6.3 ▲ **RtI**

Name _____

Convert Units of Weight and Mass

In the customary system, weight is the measure of the heaviness of an object. When converting customary units, multiply the initial measurement by a conversion factor.

Convert to the given unit. 19 lb = ___ oz

Customary Units of Weight
1 pound (lb) = 16 ounces (oz)
1 ton (T) = 2,000 pounds

Step 1 Choose a conversion factor.

16 ounces = 1 pound, so use the conversion factor $\frac{16 \text{ ounces}}{1 \text{ pound}}$.

Step 2 Multiply by the conversion factor.

So, 19 lb = 304 oz.

In the metric system, mass is the measure of the amount of matter in an object. When converting metric units, move the decimal point to multiply or divide by a power of ten.

3.1 dag = ___ mg

| kilo- | hecto- | deka- | gram | deci- | centi- | milli- |

Step 1 Start at the given unit.
Step 2 Move to the unit you are converting to.
Step 3 Move the decimal point that same number of spaces in the same direction. Fill any empty place-value positions with zeros.

So, 3.1 dag = 31,000 mg.

Convert to the given unit.

1. 43.2 dg = __0.0432__ hg
2. 4,500 pounds = __2¼__ tons
3. 3.5 grams = __3,500__ milligrams
4. 3 pounds = __48__ ounces

Chapter Resources 6-9 Reteach

Enrich 6.3

Name _____

Mixed Up Weight and Mass

The measurements in the first column were converted to other units with the results in the second column. However, the rows got mixed up. Connect each measurement in the first column with its conversion in the second column.

Original Measurements	Converted Measurements
4.6 hg	2.6 lb
0.56 lb	8.884 hg
41.6 oz	1.5 T
3,000 lb	4,600 dg
4.6 g	4,500 dg
128 oz	0.884 dag
88.4 dg	8.96 oz
2.25 T	4,600 mg
600,000 dag	6,000 lb
88.840 cg	6,000 kg
3 T	8 lb

1. Write Math Explain how you could convert ⅜ ton to ounces.
Possible answer: I can first convert ⅜ ton to 1,500 pounds. Then I can convert 1,500 pounds to 24,000 ounces.

Chapter Resources 6-10 Enrich

Metric Units The amount of matter in an object is called the mass. Metric units of mass are related by powers of 10.

Metric Units of Mass

1,000 milligrams (mg) = 1 gram (g)
100 centigrams (cg) = 1 gram
10 decigrams (dg) = 1 gram
1 dekagram (dag) = 10 grams
1 hectogram (hg) = 100 grams
1 kilogram (kg) = 1,000 grams

Example Corinne caught a trout with a mass of 2,570 grams. What was the mass of the trout in centigrams? What was the mass in kilograms?

One Way Use a conversion factor.

2,570 grams to centigrams

Choose a conversion factor.   100 cg = 1 g, so use the rate $\frac{100 \text{ cg}}{1 \text{ g}}$.

Multiply 2,570 g by the conversion factor. $\frac{2,570 \text{ g}}{1} \times \frac{100 \text{ cg}}{1 \text{ g}} = \underline{257,000}$ cg

So, the trout's mass was __257,000__ centigrams.

Another Way Use powers of 10.

Recall that metric units are related to each other by factors of 10.

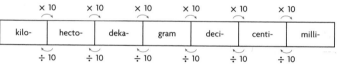

	× 10	× 10	× 10	× 10	× 10	× 10	
kilo-	hecto-	deka-	gram	deci-	centi-	milli-
	÷ 10	÷ 10	÷ 10	÷ 10	÷ 10	÷ 10	

2,570 grams to kilograms

Use the chart.

Kilograms are 3 places to the left of grams. Move the decimal point 3 places to the left.   2570.   2.570

So, 2,570 grams = __2.57__ kilograms.

Possible answer: the 1-dag object; Possible explanation: Since 10 dg = 1 g, 1 dg < 1 g. Since 1 dag = 10 g, 1 dag > 1 g. So, 1 dg < 1 dag.

Math Talk MATHEMATICAL PRACTICES ❷
Reason Quantitatively Compare objects with masses of 1 dg and 1 dag. Which has a greater mass? Explain.

2. **MATHEMATICAL PRACTICE ❶** Describe Relationships Suppose hoots and goots are units of weight, and 2 hoots = 4 goots. Which is heavier, a hoot or a goot? Explain.

a hoot; Possible explanation: Each hoot weighs 2 goots, so each goot is only half the weight of a hoot.

328

© Houghton Mifflin Harcourt Publishing Company

Metric Units Discuss the list of metric units of mass.

- **In the metric units chart, how is each unit of mass related to the unit above it?** Except for dekagrams, each unit is 10 times larger than the unit above it.

- **How is each unit of mass related to the unit below it?** Except for decigrams, each unit is 10 times smaller than the unit below it.

One Way

Point out that metric units can be converted in the same way as customary units.

- **Which units should be in the numerator and denominator of the conversion factor? Explain.** The given unit should be in the denominator so that you can divide the common unit before multiplying; grams should be in the denominator and centigrams in the numerator.

Another Way

- **Why do you divide to convert grams to kilograms?** Kilograms are larger than grams, so there will be fewer kilograms than grams.

Math Talk Use **Math Talk** to focus on students' understanding of metric units of mass. Ask: Which is the greater mass: 1 decigram or 1 gram? 1 gram

MP1 Make sense of problems and persevere in solving them. In Exercise 2, the units are imaginary units, so students must use ratio reasoning to determine which unit is heaver.

⚠ COMMON ERRORS

Error Students move the decimal point in the wrong direction when converting metric units.

Example 2,570 g = 2,570,000 kg

Springboard to Learning Refer students to the chart on page 328. Point out that if the new unit is to the right of the original unit, students should move the decimal point to the right. If the new unit is to the left of the original unit, students should move the decimal point to the left. Point out that it is helpful to decide whether the new number of units will be greater or less than the original number of units to determine if the answer is reasonable.

Advanced Learners
Visual
Individual / Partners

- Write the following problem on the board.

  A European chef melted together 2 hectograms of dark chocolate, 1 kilogram of milk chocolate, and 8 dekagrams of white chocolate. She poured half of the mixture into cake batter.

- **How many kilograms of melted chocolate does she have left?** 0.64 kg

- **Have students explain how they found their answers.** First, I converted each unit to kilograms: 2 hg = 0.2 kg; 8 dag = 0.08 kg. Next, I found the total amount of chocolate, 1.28 kg. Then, I divided the amount by 2 to find the amount left: 1.28 ÷ 2 = 0.64.

- **Find the answer again, this time in dekagrams.** 64 dag

- **Explain how you found your answer.** There are 100 dekagrams in a kilogram. Since 0.64 × 100 = 64, 0.64 kg = 64 dag.

Lesson 6.3 328

③ EXPLAIN

Share and Show

The first problem connects to the learning model. Have students use the MathBoard to explain their thinking.

Use the checked exercises for **Quick Check**. Students should show their answers for the Quick Check on the MathBoard.

 Quick Check

If → a student misses the checked exercises

Then → Differentiate Instruction with
- Reteach 6.3
- Personal Math Trainer 6.RP.A.3d
- RtI Tier 1 Activity (online)

 Use **Math Talk** to focus on students' understanding of the relationship between the metric units of capacity and mass. After students answer this question, ask them what other units of measure have these same characteristics. metric units of length

On Your Own

Observe students as they complete the problems. Ensure that they use the correct conversion factors.

Exercise 13 requires students to use higher order thinking skills.

- **How many centigrams are there in 1 decigram?** 10 centigrams **How many milligrams are there in 1 centigram?** 10 milligrams **How many milligrams are there in 1 decigram?** 100 milligrams

---

Name _____

Share and Show

Convert to the given unit.

1. 9 pounds = [ ] ounces

conversion factor: $\dfrac{16 \text{ oz}}{1 \text{ lb}}$

9 pounds = 9 lb × $\dfrac{16 \text{ oz}}{1 \text{ lb}}$ = __144__ oz

2. 3.77 grams = __0.377__ dekagram

✓ 3. Amanda's computer weighs 56 ounces. How many pounds does it weigh?

_____ $3\frac{1}{2}$ lb _____

✓ 4. A honeybee can carry 40 mg of nectar. How many grams of nectar can a honeybee carry?

_____ 0.04 g _____

Possible answer: Alike: both are based on powers of 10 and both use prefixes from milli- through kilo-. Different: they measure different properties (capacity and mass).

Math Talk | MATHEMATICAL PRACTICES ③
Compare How are metric units of capacity and mass alike? How are they different?

On Your Own

Convert to the given unit.

5. 4 lb = __64__ oz

6. 7.13 g = __713__ cg

7. 3 T = __6,000__ lb

8. The African Goliath frog can weigh up to 7 pounds. How many ounces can the Goliath frog weigh?

_____ 112 oz _____

9. _GO DEEPER_ The mass of a standard hockey puck must be at least 156 grams. What is the minimum mass of 8 hockey pucks in kilograms?

_____ 1.248 kg _____

Practice: Copy and Solve Compare. Write <, >, or =.

10. 250 lb < 0.25 T

11. 65.3 hg = 653 dag

12. 5 T > 5,000 lb

13. _THINK SMARTER_ Masses of precious stones are measured in carats, where 1 carat = 200 milligrams. What is the mass of a 50-dg diamond in carats?

_____ 25 carats _____

© Houghton Mifflin Harcourt Publishing Company

Problem Solving • Applications Real World

Use the table for 14–17.

14. Express the weight range for bowling balls in pounds.

10–16 lb

15. GO DEEPER How many more pounds does the heaviest soccer ball weigh than the heaviest baseball? Round your answer to the nearest hundredth.

0.67 lb

16. THINK SMARTER A manufacturer produces 3 tons of baseballs per day and packs them in cartons of 24 baseballs each. If all of the balls are the minimum allowable weight, how many cartons of balls does the company produce each day?

800 cartons

17. MATHEMATICAL PRACTICE ⑤ Communicate Explain how you could use mental math to estimate the number of soccer balls it would take to produce a total weight of 1 ton.

Possible answer: Soccer balls weigh about 1 pound. Since 1 T = 2,000 lb, you would need about 2,000 soccer balls to produce a total weight of 1 ton.

18. THINK SMARTER The Wilson family's newborn baby weighs 84 ounces. Choose the numbers to show the baby's weight in pounds and ounces.

⑤ 6 7 pounds   3 ④ 5 ounces

Sport Ball Weights (in ounces)	
baseball 5–5.25	handball 2.1–2.3
bowling ball 160–256	soccer ball 14–16

WRITE ➤ Math   Show Your Work

© Houghton Mifflin Harcourt Publishing Company

330

DIFFERENTIATED INSTRUCTION   INDEPENDENT ACTIVITIES

Differentiated Centers Kit

Activities
Estimating Units of Measure

Students complete online orange Activity Card 17 by choosing the appropriate unit of measure for different objects.

Literature
A Peek into a Tiny World

Students read about using a stage micrometer to make measurements of tiny creatures.

---

④ ELABORATE

Problem Solving • Applications Real World

Common Core MATHEMATICAL PRACTICES

THINK SMARTER

Exercise 16 requires students to use higher order thinking skills.

Math on the Spot Video Tutor

Use this video to help students model and solve this type of *Think Smarter* problem.

GO DIGITAL Math on the Spot videos are in the Interactive Student Edition and at *www.thinkcentral.com*.

MP5 Use appropriate tools strategically. In Exercise 18, remind students that ounces measure weight and fluid ounces measure capacity. Elicit the fact from students that 16 ounces equals 1 pound.

THINK SMARTER

Exercise 18 assesses a student's ability to use ratio reasoning to convert a unit of weight in the customary measurement system. Students who incorrectly answer this item may not have used the rate $\frac{1 \text{ lb}}{16 \text{ oz}}$ to convert from ounces to pounds. Furthermore, students may not understand that the fractional part of the answer can be renamed using the smaller unit (ounces).

⑤ EVALUATE Formative Assessment

Essential Question
Using the Language Objective
Reflect Have students work in teams to create a step-by-step information flier to answer the essential question.

How can you use ratio reasoning to convert from one unit of weight or mass to another?
I can use conversion factors to convert metric or customary units. I can also multiply or divide by powers of 10 for metric units.

Math Journal WRITE ➤ Math

Explain how you would find the number of ounces in 0.25 T.

Practice and Homework

Use the Practice and Homework pages to provide students with more practice of the concepts and skills presented in this lesson. Students master their understanding as they complete practice items and then challenge their critical thinking skills with Problem Solving. Use the Write Math section to determine student's understanding of content for this lesson. Encourage students to use their Math Journals to record their answers.

Name _____

Convert Units of Weight and Mass

 COMMON CORE STANDARD—6.RP.A.3d
Understand ratio concepts and use ratio reasoning to solve problems.

Convert to the given unit.

1. 5 pounds = ☐ ounces

conversion factor: $\frac{16 \text{ oz}}{1 \text{ lb}}$

5 pounds = 5 $\cancel{lb}$ × $\frac{16 \text{ oz}}{1 \cancel{lb}}$ = 80oz

2. 2.36 grams = ☐ hectograms

Move the decimal point 2 places to the left.

2.36 grams = 0.0236 hectogram

3. 30 g = ☐ dg

_____300_____

4. 17.2 hg = ☐ g

_____1,720_____

5. 400 lb = ☐ T

_____0.2_____

6. 38,600 mg = ☐ dag

_____3.86_____

7. 87 oz = ☐ lb ☐ oz

_____5; 7_____

8. 0.65 T = ☐ lb

_____1,300_____

Problem Solving Real World

9. Maggie bought 52 ounces of swordfish selling for $6.92 per pound. What was the total cost?

_____$22.49_____

10. Three bunches of grapes have masses of 1,000 centigrams, 1,000 decigrams, and 1,000 grams, respectively. What is the total combined mass of the grapes in kilograms?

_____1.11 kg_____

11. **WRITE** ▸*Math* Explain how you would find the number of ounces in 0.25T.

Possible answer: Convert 0.25 tons to pounds, then convert the pounds to ounces.

© Houghton Mifflin Harcourt Publishing Company

 **PROFESSIONAL DEVELOPMENT** **Math Talk in Action**

Teacher:	Look at Exercise 7. When you convert ounces to pounds, are you converting a larger unit to a smaller unit, or a smaller unit to a larger unit? Explain.
Joaquim:	A smaller unit to a larger unit because a pound contains 16 ounces, so ounces are smaller than pounds.
Teacher:	What conversion factor would you use to change ounces to pounds? Why?
Hideo:	Since 1 pound = 16 ounces, I would multiply 87 ounces by the conversion factor $\frac{1 \text{ pound}}{16 \text{ ounces}}$ to find the number of pounds. Ounces in the numerator and ounces in the denominator will simplify to 1, leaving the answer in pounds.

Teacher:	Can 87 be divided evenly by 16? If not, what does the remainder mean?
Anna-Marie:	No, it does not divide evenly. The remainder is the number of ounces left after the ounces are divided into pounds. 87 ounces is equal to 5 full pounds and 7 more ounces.
Teacher:	Can anyone think of another way to solve the problem?
Brendan:	I would use subtraction and subtract 16 from 87 five times. Whatever amount is left I would leave in ounces.

Lesson Check (6.RP.A.3d)

1. The mass of Denise's rock sample is 684 grams. The mass of Pauline's rock sample is 29,510 centigrams. How much greater is the mass of Denise's sample than Pauline's sample?

_____ 38,890 centigrams _____

2. A sign at the entrance to a bridge reads: Maximum allowable weight 2.25 tons. Jason's truck weighs 2,150 pounds. How much additional weight can he carry?

_____ 2,350 pounds _____

Spiral Review (6.RP.A.1, 6.RP.A.2, 6.RP.A.3a, 6.RP.A.3b, 6.RP.A.3c)

3. There are 23 students in a math class. Twelve of them are boys. What is the ratio of girls to total number of students?

_____ 11 to 23 _____

4. Miguel hiked 3 miles in 54 minutes. At this rate, how long will it take him to hike 5 miles?

_____ 90 minutes _____

5. Marco borrowed $150 from his brother. He has paid back 30% so far. How much money does Marco still owe his brother?

_____ $105 _____

6. How many milliliters are equivalent to 2.7 liters?

_____ 2,700 milliliters _____

© Houghton Mifflin Harcourt Publishing Company

FOR MORE PRACTICE GO TO THE Personal Math Trainer

Continue concepts and skills practice with Lesson Check. Use Spiral Review to engage students in previously taught concepts and to promote content retention. Common Core standards are correlated to each section.

Mid-Chapter Checkpoint

LESSONS 6.1 TO 6.3

Formative Assessment

Use the **Mid-Chapter Checkpoint** to assess students' learning and progress in the first half of the chapter. The formative assessment provides the opportunity to adjust teaching methods for individual or whole class instruction.

Name _____

✓ Mid-Chapter Checkpoint

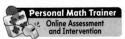
Personal Math Trainer
Online Assessment
and Intervention

Vocabulary

Choose the best term from the box to complete the sentence.

Vocabulary
capacity
conversion factor
metric system

1. A __conversion factor__ is a rate in which the two quantities are equal, but use different units. (p. 315)

2. __Capacity__ is the amount a container can hold. (p. 321)

Concepts and Skills

Convert units to solve. (6.RP.A.3d)

3. A professional football field is 160 feet wide. What is the width of the field in yards?

$$53\frac{1}{3} \text{ yd}$$

4. Julia drinks 8 cups of water per day. How many quarts of water does she drink per day?

2 qt

5. The mass of Hinto's math book is 4,458 grams. What is the mass of 4 math books in kilograms?

17.832 kg

6. Turning off the water while brushing your teeth saves 379 centiliters of water. How many liters of water can you save if you turn off the water the next 3 times you brush your teeth?

11.37 L

Convert to the given unit. (6.RP.A.3d)

7. 34.2 mm = __3.42__ cm

8. 42 in. = $3\frac{1}{2}$ ft

9. 1.4 km = __14__ hm

10. 4 gal = __16__ qt

11. 53 dL = __0.53__ daL

12. 28 c = __14__ pt

© Houghton Mifflin Harcourt Publishing Company

✓ **Data-Driven Decision Making**  RtI

Based on the results of the Mid-Chapter Checkpoint, use the following resources to strengthen individual or whole class instruction.

Item	Lesson	Standard	Content Focus	Personal Math Trainer	Intervene With
3, 7, 8, 9	6.1	6.RP.A.3d	Convert units of length.	6.RP.A.3d	R—6.1
4, 6, 10, 11, 12	6.2	6.RP.A.3d	Convert units of capacity.	6.RP.A.3d	R—6.2
5	6.3	6.RP.A.3d	Convert units of weight and mass.	6.RP.A.3d	R—6.3

Key: R—Reteach (in the *Chapter Resources*)

13. Trenton's laptop is 32 centimeters wide. What is the width of the laptop in decimeters? (6.RP.A.3d)

_____
3.2 decimeters

14. A truck is carrying 8 cars weighing an average of 4,500 pounds each. What is the total weight in tons of the cars on the truck? (6.RP.A.3d)

_____
18 tons

15. GO DEEPER Ben's living room is a rectangle measuring 10 yards by 168 inches. By how many feet does the length of the room exceed the width? (6.RP.A.3d)

_____
16 feet

16. Jessie served 13 pints of orange juice at her party. How many quarts of orange juice did she serve? (6.RP.A.3d)

_____
6 quarts 1 pint

17. Kaylah's cell phone has a mass of 50,000 centigrams. What is the mass of her phone in grams? (6.RP.A.3d)

_____
500 grams

© Houghton Mifflin Harcourt Publishing Company

334

✓ Data-Driven Decision Making  RtI

Item	Lesson	Standard	Content Focus	Personal Math Trainer	Intervene with
13, 15	6.1	6.RP.A.3d	Convert units of length.	6.RP.A.3d	R—6.1
17	6.3	6.RP.A.3d	Convert units of weight and mass.	6.RP.A.3d	R—6.3
14, 17	6.2	6.RP.A.3d	Convert units of capacity.	6.RP.A.3d	R—6.2

Key: R—Reteach (in the *Chapter Resources*)

Transform Units

LESSON AT A GLANCE

F C R Focus:

Common Core State Standards

6.RP.A.3d Use ratio and rate reasoning to solve real-world and mathematical problems, e.g., by reasoning about tables of equivalent ratios, tape diagrams, double number line diagrams, or equations.
Use ratio reasoning to convert measurement units; manipulate and transform units appropriately when multiplying or dividing quantities.

MATHEMATICAL PRACTICES
MP1 Make sense of problems and persevere in solving them. **MP3** Construct viable arguments and critique the reasoning of others. **MP5** Use appropriate tools strategically.

F C R Coherence:

Standards Across the Grades
Before	Grade 6	After
5.MD.A.1	6.RP.A.3d	7.RP.A.1

F C R Rigor:

Level 1: Understand Concepts....................*Share and Show* (✓ Checked Items)
Level 2: Procedural Skills and Fluency.......*On Your Own*
Level 3: Applications.................................*Think Smarter and Go Deeper*

Learning Objective
Transform units to solve problems.

Language Objective
Students write in their Math Journal the steps to transform units to solve problems.

Materials
MathBoard

F C R For more about how *GO Math!* fosters **Coherence** within the Content Standards and Mathematical Progressions for this chapter, see page 313H.

About the Math
Professional Development

MP2 Reason abstractly and quantitatively.

In this lesson, students continue to develop their ability to reason quantitatively as they learn to manipulate and transform units to solve problems. Students learn how to look at rates, such as 12 inches per foot, abstractly (12 to 1) as well as in context (inches per foot).

The skills students need to transform units are the same whether the context involves a simple unit conversion or applying a rate such as boxes per minute. To help students decontextualize and contextualize situations involving rate, ask them to write 3 different rates that use the numbers in the ratio $\frac{12}{1}$; for example, 12 inches per foot, 12 bracelets per hour, and 12 people per row. Then have students work together to pose and solve a problem for each context. Discuss the solution for each problem. Stress that the method of finding the answer is the same even though the contexts are different.

 Professional Development Videos

 **Interactive Student Edition**

 **Personal Math Trainer**

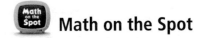 **Math on the Spot**

*i***T** *i*Tools: Measurement

Daily Routines

Common Core

 **Problem of the Day 6.4**

Marty found that 55% of the students in his class walked to school. What fraction of the class did not walk to school? $\frac{9}{20}$

- Interactive Student Edition
- Multimedia eGlossary

Fluency Builder

Factoring. Have students list all of the factors of each number.

1. 36   1, 2, 3, 4, 6, 9, 12, 18, 36

2. 64   1, 2, 4, 8, 16, 32, 64

3. 145   1, 5, 29, 145

4. 225   1, 3, 5, 9, 15, 25, 45, 75, 225

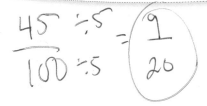

1 ENGAGE

with the Interactive Student Edition

Essential Question

How can you transform units to solve problems?

Making Connections

Discuss conversion factors with students.

- **Why would you use a conversion factor?** to convert from one measurement unit to another

Learning Activity

Give students this problem: How many quarts are there in 12 gallons?

- **What is the conversion factor to convert from gallons to quarts?** $\frac{4 \text{ quarts}}{1 \text{ gallon}}$

- **How can you use the conversion factor to solve the problem?** Multiply 12 gallons by the conversion factor: 12 gallons $\times \frac{4 \text{ quarts}}{1 \text{ gallon}} =$ 48 quarts

Literacy and Mathematics

Have students make a chart showing conversion factors. Have them include both customary and metric units of length, capacity, and weight/mass.

- Then have students work in groups to write real-world problems which involve customary and metric units of length, capacity, and weight/mass. Have them show a conversion factor that can be used to solve each problem.

② EXPLORE

Unlock the Problem

Common Core **MATHEMATICAL PRACTICES**

Have students read the problem.

MP1 Make sense of problems and persevere in solving them.

- **How can you identify the units in the problem?** Find the quantities that are measurements.

- **How do you know that the answer will have units of miles?** The problem asks how many miles Maria can travel.

- **What does *per* mean in the rate 20 miles per gallon?** Possible answer: for each **How can you write this rate as a fraction?** $\frac{20 \text{ miles}}{1 \text{ gallon}}$

MP2 Reason abstractly and quantitatively.

- **What if Maria used $\frac{1}{2}$ gallon of gas? Would you expect the number of miles she traveled to be greater than or less than 20? Explain.** Less than 20; if Maria used $\frac{1}{2}$ gallon of gas, she used less than 1 gallon, so she traveled less than 20 miles.

MP4 Model with mathematics.

- **What if Maria's car has a gas mileage of 40 miles per gallon? If she uses 9 gallons, would you expect the number of miles she traveled to be greater than or less than 180?** Greater than 180; instead of multiplying 20 times 9, multiply 40 times 9.

 Strategy:
Identify Relationships

Tell students that Katie walks three miles per hour.

- Explain that this is Katie's rate.

- Discuss with students the average rates of a bicycle (10 mph), car (30 mph), and train (50 mph). Compare these rates with the rate at which Katie walks.

- Have pairs of students use the given rate to determine how far Katie walks in 3 hours.
  9 miles

6.RP.A.3d Use ratio and rate reasoning to solve real-world and mathematical problems, e.g., by reasoning about tables of equivalent ratios, tape diagrams, double number line diagrams, or equations. Use ratio reasoning to convert measurement units; manipulate and transform units appropriately when multiplying or dividing quantities.

Name _____

Lesson 6.4

Transform Units

Essential Question How can you transform units to solve problems?

Common Core **Ratios and Proportional Relationships—6.RP.A.3d**

MATHEMATICAL PRACTICES
MP1, MP3, MP6

You can sometimes use the units of the quantities in a problem to help you decide how to solve the problem.

Unlock the Problem

A car's gas mileage is the average distance the car can travel on 1 gallon of gas. Maria's car has a gas mileage of 20 miles per gallon. How many miles can Maria travel on 9 gallons of gas?

> • Would you expect the answer to be greater or less than 20 miles? Why?
>
> **Possible answer: greater than; Maria can go 20 mi on 1 gal, so she can go much farther on 9 gal.**

 Analyze the units in the problem.

STEP 1 Identify the units.

You know two quantities: the car's gas mileage and the amount of gas.

Gas mileage: 20 miles per gallon $= \dfrac{20 \text{ miles}}{1 \text{ gallon}}$

Amount of gas: 9 ____**gallons**____

You want to know a third quantity: the distance the car can travel.

Distance: ▓ ____**miles**____

STEP 2 Determine the relationship among the units.

Think: The answer needs to have units of miles. If I multiply $\frac{20 \text{ miles}}{1 \text{ gallon}}$ by 9 gallons, I can simplify the units. The product will have units of

____**miles**____ , which is what I want.

STEP 3 Use the relationship.

$$\frac{20 \text{ mi}}{1 \text{ gal}} \times 9 \text{ gal} = \frac{20 \text{ mi}}{1 \text{ gal}} \times \frac{9 \text{ gal}}{1} = \underline{\text{180 mi}}$$

So, Maria can travel ____**180 miles**____ on 9 gallons of gas.

1. Explain why the units of gallons are crossed out in the multiplication step above.

   Possible answer: Since the same unit is in the numerator and in the denominator, they simplify to 1.

© Houghton Mifflin Harcourt Publishing Company

Reteach 6.4 ▲ RtI

Name _____

Transform Units

To solve problems involving different units, use the relationship among units to help you set up a multiplication problem.

> Green peppers are on sale for $1.80 per pound. How much would 2.5 pounds of green peppers cost?
>
> **Step 1** Identify the units.
>
> You know two quantities: pounds of peppers and total cost. You want to know the cost of 2.5 pounds.
>
> $1.80 per lb $= \frac{\$1.80}{1 \text{ lb}}$
>
> **Step 2** Determine the relationship among the units.
>
> The answer needs to be in dollars. Set up the multiplication problem so that pounds will simplify to 1.
>
> $\frac{\$1.80}{1 \text{ lb}} \times 2.5 \text{ lb} = \frac{\$1.80}{1 \text{ lb}} \times \frac{2.5 \text{ lb}}{1} = \$4.50$
>
> **Step 3** Use the relationship.
>
> So, 2.5 pounds of peppers will cost $4.50.

Solve.

1. If 2 bags of cherries cost $5.50, how much do 7 bags cost?

   a. What are you trying to find?
      cost of 7 bags

   b. Set up the problem.
      $\frac{\$5.50}{2 \text{ bags}} \times \frac{7 \text{ bags}}{1}$

   c. What is the cost of 7 bags?
      $19.25

2. The area of a living room is 24 square yards. If the width is 12 feet, what is the length of the living room in yards?

   a. What is the width in yards?
      $12 \text{ ft} \times \frac{1 \text{ yd}}{3 \text{ ft}} = 4 \text{ yd}$

   b. Set up the problem.
      $\frac{24 \text{ yd} \times \text{yd}}{4 \text{ yd}}$

   c. What is the length in yards?
      6 yd

Enrich 6.4 — Differentiated Instruction

Name _____

Missing Pieces

For each problem, an answer is given. Fill in the blanks with numbers, units, or both.

1. $\frac{21 \text{ L}}{1 \text{ hr}} \times \blacksquare = 84 \text{ L}$

   4 hr

2. $\frac{36 \text{ kg}}{10 \text{ hr}} \times \frac{24 \text{ hr}}{1 \text{ day}} \times \blacksquare \text{ days} = 259.2 \text{ kg}$

   3

3. 225 sq m ÷ ▓ = 9 m

   25 m

4. $\frac{18 \text{ cm}}{1 \text{ min}} \times \frac{1 \text{ m}}{100 \text{ cm}} \times \frac{60 \text{ min}}{1 \text{ hr}} \times \blacksquare = \frac{43.2 \text{ m}}{1 \text{ hr}}$

   4

5. $\frac{6 \text{ gal}}{1 \text{ day}} \times \frac{7 \text{ days}}{1 \text{ week}} \times \blacksquare = 168 \text{ gal}$

   4 weeks

6. 108 eeks $\times \frac{1 \text{ eep}}{18 \text{ eeks}} \times \frac{1 \blacksquare}{4 \text{ eeps}} = 1.5 \text{ bleps}$

   blep

7. **Write Math** Explain how you solved Problem 6.
   Possible answer: First, I wrote 108 eeks as $\frac{108 \text{ eeks}}{1}$. Since eeks appears once in a numerator and once in a denominator, they divide out. Eeps also divide out because they appear once in the numerator and once in the denominator. Since the answer contains bleps, I knew that bleps had to be in the numerator of the third ratio.

Sometimes you may need to convert units before solving a problem.

 Example

The material for a rectangular awning has an area of 315 square feet. If the width of the material is 5 yards, what is the length of the material in feet? (Recall that the area of a rectangle is equal to its length times its width.)

STEP 1 Identify the units.

You know two quantities: the area of the material and the width of the material.

Area: 315 sq ft = 315 ft × ft

Width: 5 __yd__

You want to know a third quantity: the length of the material.

Length: ▇ ft

> **Math Idea**
> You can write units of area as products.
> sq ft = ft × ft

STEP 2 Determine the relationship among the units.

Think: The answer needs to have units of feet. So, I should convert the width from yards to feet.

Width: $\dfrac{5\,yd}{1} \times \dfrac{3\,ft}{1\,yd} = $ __15__ ft

Think: If I divide the area by the width, the units will simplify. The quotient will have units of __feet__, which is what I want.

STEP 3 Use the relationship.

Divide the area by the width to find the length.

315 sq ft ÷ __15__ ft

Write the division using a fraction bar.

$\dfrac{315\ \text{sq ft}}{15\ \text{ft}}$

Write the units of area as a product and divide the common units.

$\dfrac{315\ \text{ft} \times \text{ft}}{15\ \text{ft}} = $ __21__ ft

So, the length of the material is __21 feet__.

Possible answer: Looking at the units can help you decide whether to multiply or divide so that the answer will have the units you want.

 Math Talk

MATHEMATICAL PRACTICES ①
Analyze How can examining the units in a problem help you solve the problem?

2. **MATHEMATICAL PRACTICE ③** Apply Explain how knowing how to find the area of a rectangle could help you solve the problem above.

Possible answer: To find the area of a rectangle, multiply the length and width. If the area and width are known, you can divide to find the length.

3. **MATHEMATICAL PRACTICE ⑥** Explain why the answer is in feet.

Possible answer: The area of the material is in sq ft, which can be written as ft × ft. So, two factors in the numerator have the unit, feet. Since only one factor of feet is a common unit in the numerator and denominator, one of the factors of feet will remain in the answer when you simplify the common unit to 1.

336

© Houghton Mifflin Harcourt Publishing Company • Image Credits: (t) Victoria Smith/HRW

Advanced Learners

Interpersonal / Social
Small Group / Partners

- Have students make a set of 5 to 10 "context" cards that can be used to create rates; for example, books per week, animals per day, etc.

- Have students make a set of 5 to 10 "ratio" cards; for example, 45 to 1, 16 to 1, 7 to 1, etc.

- Have groups shuffle together the context cards and place them in a stack. Repeat with the ratio cards.

- Instruct students to take turns choosing a card from each stack and using the information to write and solve a word problem. For example, if the context card is books per week and the ratio card is 16 to 1, students might write this problem:

Tony's class reads 16 books per week. How many books does the class read in 6 weeks? 96 books

---

Example

Have students read the problem. Write the formula for the area of a rectangle $A = l \times w$ on the board for students to reference as they solve the problem.

- **What conversion factor do you need to solve the problem?** $\frac{3\,ft}{1\,yd}$ **How do you know?** The width is in yards, and the problem asks for the length in feet. I have to convert yards to feet.

Have students look at Step 2.

- **Why can you divide the units of yards?** There are yards in a numerator and a denominator, and I can simplify the common units.

Have students look at Step 3.

- **Why do you divide the area by the width?** To find the area of a rectangle, I multiply length times width. So, to find the length of a rectangle, I can divide its area by the width.

- **Why does it makes sense that sq ft = ft × ft given the area formula $A = l \times w$?** Possible answer: Area is given in square units, and length and width are given in units. If the length of a rectangle is 5 ft and the width is 6 ft, the area is 30 sq ft because 5 × 6 = 30 and ft × ft = sq ft.

MP3 Construct viable arguments and critique the reasoning of others. In Exercise 2, first have students describe the relationship between the area, width, and length of a rectangle.

MP6 Attend to precision. In Exercise 3, have students explain why the answer is in feet even though the width was given in yards.

⚠ **COMMON ERRORS**

Error Students incorrectly set up problems involving unit transformations.

Example A car gets 20 miles per gallon. How many miles can the car travel on 4 gallons of gas?

$\dfrac{20\ mi}{1\ gal} \div 4\ gal = \dfrac{20\ \cancel{mi}}{1\ \cancel{gal}} \div \dfrac{4\ \cancel{gal}}{1} = 5\ mi$

Springboard to Learning Remind students that they can simplify the units to 1 only if the same unit appears in both a numerator and a denominator when *multiplying* two fractions or ratios. Encourage them to check their answer to be sure it is reasonable. For example, in the problem above, if the car gets 20 miles per gallon, it can travel more than 20 miles on 4 gallons, so the answer should be greater than 20 miles, not less.

Share and Show

Use the checked exercises for **Quick Check**. Students should use their MathBoards to show their solutions. Encourage students to circle the quantities given in each problem.

Have students discuss how examining the units in Exercises 2 and 3 helped them solve these problems.

If ➤ a student misses the checked exercises

Then ➤ **Differentiate Instruction** with
- Reteach 6.4
- Personal Math Trainer 6.RP.A.3d
- RtI Tier 1 Activity (online)

On Your Own

For Exercises 7–8, encourage students to make sure that their answer is in the units asked for in the problem.

MP1 Make sense of problems and persevere in solving them. For Exercise 8, students will need to divide the total number of boxes by the number of boxes per minute to find the number of minutes it takes.

Personal Math Trainer

Be sure to assign Exercise 9 to students in the Personal Math Trainer. It features a video to help them model and answer the problem. Students who incorrectly answer 9b may not have realized that they need to convert the length from centimeters to meters before they can determine the width in meters. Furthermore, students must understand that if the area and length of the pool are known, they can divide to find the width of the pool.

Name _____

Share and Show [MATH BOARD]

1. A dripping faucet leaks 12 gallons of water per day. How many gallons does the faucet leak in 6 days?

Quantities you know: $\dfrac{12 \text{ gal}}{1 \text{ day}}$ and __6__ days

Quantity you want to know: ■ ____ gallons

$$\dfrac{12 \text{ gal}}{1 \text{ day}} \times 6 \text{ days} = \underline{72 \text{ gal}}$$

So, the faucet leaks __72 gallons__ in 6 days.

2. Bananas sell for $0.44 per pound. How much will 7 pounds of bananas cost?

$3.08

3. Grizzly Park is a rectangular park with an area of 24 square miles. The park is 3 miles wide. What is its length in miles?

8 miles

On Your Own

Multiply or divide the quantities.

4. $\dfrac{24 \text{ kg}}{1 \text{ min}} \times 15 \text{ min}$

360 kg

5. $216 \text{ sq cm} \div 8 \text{ cm}$

27 cm

6. $\dfrac{17 \text{ L}}{1 \text{ hr}} \times 9 \text{ hr}$

153 L

7. **GO DEEPER** The rectangular rug in Marcia's living room measures 12 feet by 108 inches. What is the rug's area in square feet?

108 square feet

8. **MATHEMATICAL PRACTICE ①** **Make Sense of Problems** A box-making machine makes cardboard boxes at a rate of 72 boxes per minute. How many minutes does it take to make 360 boxes?

5 minutes

Personal Math Trainer

9. **THINK SMARTER +** The area of an Olympic-size swimming pool is 1,250 square meters. The length of the pool is 5,000 centimeters. Select True or False for each statement.

9a. The length of the pool is 50 meters. ● True ○ False

9b. The width of the pool is 25 meters. ● True ○ False

9c. The area of the pool is 1.25 square kilometers ○ True ● False

© Houghton Mifflin Harcourt Publishing Company

Make Predictions

A *prediction* is a guess about something in the future. A prediction is more likely to be accurate if it is based on facts and logical reasoning.

The Hoover Dam is one of America's largest producers of hydroelectric power. Up to 300,000 gallons of water can move through the dam's generators every second. Predict the amount of water that moves through the generators in half of an hour.

FACT		PREDICTION
300,000 gallons per second	$\rightarrow$	? gallons in half of an hour

Use what you know about transforming units to make a prediction.

You know the rate of the water through the generators, and you are given an amount of time.

Rate of flow: $\dfrac{300{,}000 \text{ gal}}{1 \text{ sec}}$; time: $\dfrac{1}{2}$ hr

You want to find the amount of water.

Amount of water: gallons

Convert the amount of time to seconds to match the units in the rate.

$\dfrac{1}{2}$ hr = __30__ min

$$\dfrac{30 \text{ min}}{1} \times \dfrac{60 \text{ sec}}{1 \text{ min}} = \underline{1{,}800} \text{ sec}$$

Multiply the rate by the amount of time to find the amount of water.

$$\dfrac{300{,}000 \text{ gal}}{\text{sec}} \times \dfrac{1{,}800 \text{ sec}}{1} = 540{,}000{,}000 \text{ gal}$$

So, a good prediction of the amount of water that moves through the generators in half of an hour is ___540,000,000 gallons___.

Transform units to solve.

10. An average of 19,230 people tour the Hoover Dam each week. Predict the number of people touring the dam in a year.

999,960 people

11. **THINK SMARTER** The Hoover Dam generates an average of about 11,506,000 kilowatt-hours of electricity per day. Predict the number of kilowatt-hours generated in 7 weeks.

563,794,000 kilowatt-hours

© Houghton Mifflin Harcourt Publishing Company • Image Credits: (t) ©Ron Chapple Stock/Alamy Images

---

DIFFERENTIATED INSTRUCTION   INDEPENDENT ACTIVITIES

Differentiated Centers Kit

Activities
Estimating Units of Measure

Students complete online orange Activity Card 17 by choosing the appropriate unit of measure for different objects.

Literature
A Peek into a Tiny World

Students read about using a stage micrometer to make measurements of tiny creatures.

---

⁴ ELABORATE

Connect to Reading

Have students read the text about making predictions and the Hoover Dam.

- **Why is the answer of 540,000,000 gallons just a prediction?** The rate, 300,000 gal per sec, is an estimate of the amount of water that will move through the dam each second.

Refer students to Exercise 11.

- **How can you determine your answer is reasonable?** Possible answer: If the dam generates between 11 and 12 million kilowatt-hours of hydroelectricity per day, it should generate about 50 times that amount in 7 weeks, or 49 days. $50 \times 11 = 550$ million and $50 \times 12 = 600$ million. Since 563,794,000 is between 550 and 600 million, the answer is reasonable.

Math on the Spot Video Tutor
Use this video to help students model and solve this type of *Think Smarter* problem.

GO DIGITAL **Math on the Spot** videos are in the Interactive Student Edition and at *www.thinkcentral.com*.

---

⁵ EVALUATE Formative Assessment

Essential Question

Using the Language Objective
Reflect Have students write the steps in their Math Journal to answer the Essential Question.

How can you transform units to solve problems? I can multiply or divide the quantities given in a problem so that common units can be simplified to 1, leaving only the units of the quantity I am trying to find.

Math Journal **WRITE** ▸Math

Write and solve a problem in which you have to transform units. Use the rate 45 people per hour in your problem.

Practice and Homework

Use the Practice and Homework pages to provide students with more practice of the concepts and skills presented in this lesson. Students master their understanding as they complete practice items and then challenge their critical thinking skills with Problem Solving. Use the Write Math section to determine student's understanding of content for this lesson. Encourage students to use their Math Journals to record their answers.

COMMON CORE STANDARD—6.RP.A.3d
Understand ratio concepts and use ratio reasoning to solve problems.

Multiply or divide the quantities.

1. $\frac{62\,g}{1\,day} \times 4$ days

   $\frac{62\,g}{1\,day} \times \frac{4\,days}{1} = 248\ g$

2. 322 sq yd ÷ 23 yd

   $\frac{322\,sq\,yd}{23\,yd}$

   $\frac{322\,yd \times yd}{23\,yd} = 14\ yd$

3. $\frac{128\,kg}{1\,hr} \times 10$ hr

   _____1,280 kg_____

4. 136 sq km ÷ 8 km

   _____17 km_____

5. $\frac{88\,lb}{1\,day} \times 12$ days

   _____1,056 lb_____

6. 154 sq mm ÷ 11 mm

   _____14 mm_____

7. $\frac{\$150}{1\,sq\,ft} \times 20$ sq ft

   _____$3,000_____

8. 234 sq ft ÷ 18 ft

   _____13 ft_____

Problem Solving Real World

9. Green grapes are on sale for $2.50 a pound. How much will 9 pounds cost?

   _____$22.50_____

10. A car travels 32 miles for each gallon of gas. How many gallons of gas does it need to travel 192 miles?

    _____6 gal_____

11. **WRITE** ▸*Math* Write and solve a problem in which you have to transform units. Use the rate 45 people per hour in your question.

    Check students' work. _____

    _____

    _____

Extend the Math   Activity

Transforming Units in Volume Problems

Investigate In this activity, students use conversion factors to transform units in a problem involving volume.

- Present the following problem to students.

  The volume of a rectangular box is 600 cubic feet. The length of the box is 10 ft. The width of the box is 12 ft. What is the height of the box in feet?

- Explain that students can use what they know about transforming units to solve the problem.
- Write the formula for the volume of a rectangular prism on the board: $V = l \times w \times h$.
- Discuss how the formula can help students find the missing height. Have students first multiply the length and width. 10 ft × 12 ft = 120 sq ft Explain that if students divide the volume by this product, the quotient will be the height of the box.

- Have students find the height of the box. Emphasize that units of cubic feet can be written ft × ft × ft.

  600 cu ft ÷ 120 sq ft = $\frac{600\ ft \times ft \times ft}{120\ ft \times ft}$ = 5 ft

Summarize Have students explain how they know that their answer is reasonable, and have them suggest a method of checking their answer. Possible answer: My answer is reasonable because after I simplified the common units in the numerator and denominator, I was left with units of feet in the answer, and this is the correct unit for the height. I could check my answer by multiplying the length, width, and height and seeing if the answer is 600 cubic feet. 10 ft × 12 ft × 5 ft = 600 cu ft

Lesson Check (6.RP.A.3d)

1. A rectangular parking lot has an area of 682 square yards. The lot is 22 yards wide. What is the length of the parking lot?

2. A machine assembles 44 key chains per hour. How many key chains does the machine assemble in 11 hours?

31 yards

484 key chains

Spiral Review (6.RP.A.3a, 6.RP.A.3c)

3. Three of these ratios are equivalent to $\frac{8}{20}$. Which one is NOT equivalent?

$\frac{2}{5}$ $\frac{12}{24}$ $\frac{16}{40}$ $\frac{40}{100}$

$\frac{12}{24}$

4. The graph shows the money that Marco earns for different numbers of days worked. How much money does he earn per day?

Money Earned

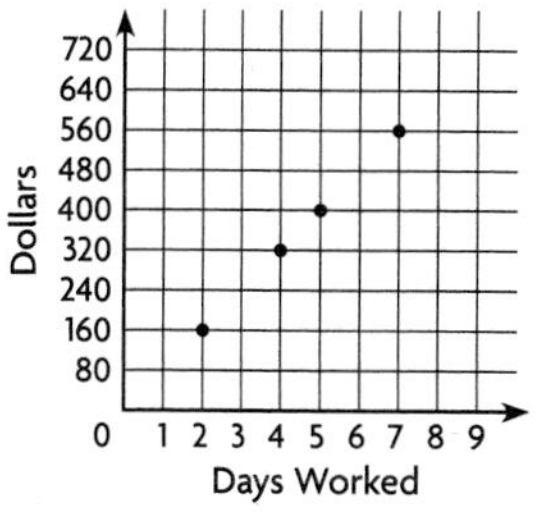

_$80_

5. Megan answered 18 questions correctly on a test. That is 75% of the total number of questions. How many questions were on the test?

24 questions

© Houghton Mifflin Harcourt Publishing Company

FOR MORE PRACTICE
GO TO THE
Personal Math Trainer

Continue concepts and skills practice with Lesson Check. Use Spiral Review to engage students in previously taught concepts and to promote content retention. Common Core standards are correlated to each section.

Problem Solving • Distance, Rate, and Time Formulas

LESSON AT A GLANCE

FOCUS COHERENCE RIGOR

F C R Focus:

Common Core State Standards

6.RP.A.3d Use ratio and rate reasoning to solve real-world and mathematical problems, e.g., by reasoning about tables of equivalent ratios, tape diagrams, double number line diagrams, or equations. Use ratio reasoning to convert measurement units; manipulate and transform units appropriately when multiplying or dividing quantities.

MATHEMATICAL PRACTICES
MP1 Make sense of problems and persevere in solving them. **MP7** Look for and make use of structure.

F C R Coherence:

Standards Across the Grades
Before   **Grade 6**   **After**
5.MD.A.1   6.RP.A.3d   7.RP.A.1

F C R Rigor:

Level 1: Understand Concepts...................*Share and Show* (✓ Checked Items)
Level 2: Procedural Skills and Fluency.......*On Your Own*
Level 3: Applications................................*Think Smarter and Go Deeper*

Learning Objective
Solve problems involving distance, rate, and time by applying the strategy *use a formula*.

Language Objective
Students review and rephrase examples from the lesson that use the strategy *use a formula* to solve problems involving distance, rate, and time.

Materials
MathBoard

F C R For more about how *GO Math!* fosters **Coherence** within the Content Standards and Mathematical Progressions for this chapter, see page 313H.

About the Math
Professional Development

Teaching for Depth

In this lesson, students use three different formulas representing the relationships among distance, rate, and time. Remind them that a rate is a ratio of two quantities that have different units of measure, and a unit rate has 1 unit in the denominator. For example, the rate $\frac{20 \text{ mi}}{2 \text{ hr}}$ is equal to the unit rate $\frac{10 \text{ mi}}{1 \text{ hr}}$.

Show examples of the formulas. Include units of distance, rate, and time, and show how to divide out common units.

$$d = r \times t \qquad\qquad r = d \div t$$

$$20 \text{ mi} = \frac{10 \text{ mi}}{1 \text{ hr}} \times \frac{2 \text{ hr}}{1} \qquad \frac{10 \text{ mi}}{1 \text{ hr}} = 20 \text{ mi} \div 2 \text{ hr}$$

$$t = d \div r$$

$$2 \text{ hr} = 20 \text{ mi} \div \frac{10 \text{ mi}}{1 \text{ hr}}$$

$$2 \text{ hr} = 20 \text{ mi} \times \frac{1 \text{ hr}}{10 \text{ mi}}$$

 Professional Development Videos

GO DIGITAL

 Interactive Student Edition

 Personal Math Trainer

 Math on the Spot

 Animated Math Models

Daily Routines
Common Core

 Problem of the Day 6.5

Marco's painting has an area of 320 square inches. If the width of the painting is 16 inches, what is the length of the painting? 20 inches

Vocabulary

 • Interactive Student Edition
• Multimedia eGlossary

Fluency Builder

Common Core Fluency
Standard 6.NS.B.3

Materials eTeacher Resources pages TR134–TR136

Operations Have students divide whole numbers and decimals.

1. 208 ÷ 4 52 **2.** 1,512 ÷ 36 42

3. 154 ÷ 44 3.5 or $3\frac{1}{2}$ **4.** 6 ÷ 24 0.25 or $\frac{1}{4}$

5. 8.2 ÷ 2 4.1 **6.** 132 ÷ 2.4 55

1 ENGAGE

with the Interactive Student Edition

Essential Question

How can you use the strategy *use a formula* to solve problems involving distance, rate, and time?

Making Connections

Migration is a seasonal movement from one place to another. Ask students what they know about bird migration.

- **Why do birds migrate?** Possible answers: for survival, climate changes, food sources, safer habitats, avoiding predators

- **To find how long it will take a bird to migrate from one location to another, what information is needed?** The distance between the locations and how fast the bird flies

Learning Activity

What is the problem the students are trying to solve? Connect the story to the problem.

- **How many minutes did Pamela fly around the park before taking a break?** 25 minutes

- **At what rate can Pamela usually fly?** 800 meters per minute

- **What are you trying to find?** how far Pamela flew

Literacy and Mathematics

View the lesson opener with the students. Have students complete the following activity after they complete the lesson.

- Have students work in groups to write a story that involves distance, rate, and time. Their stories should include an explanation of how distance is affected if speed increases.

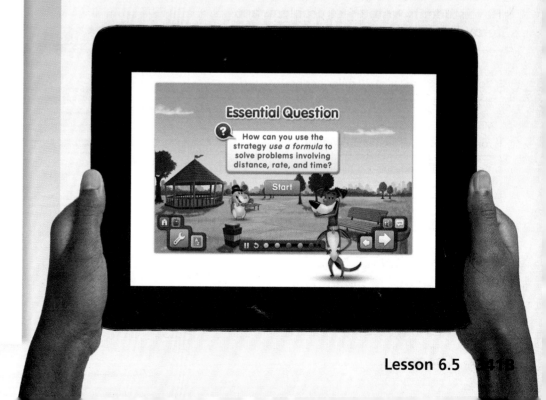

2 EXPLORE

Present or have students read the introductory paragraph and then ask:

- **Why are the variables *d*, *r*, and *t* good choices for distance, rate, and time?** Possible answer: It is easy to remember what they represent because they are the first letters of the words.

Unlock the Problem

 **MATHEMATICAL PRACTICES**

To introduce the lesson, have students watch the Real World Video.

Direct students' attention to the question, "How long does the trip take?"

- **The question starts with the words "How long." Is the question asking for a distance or an amount of time?** an amount of time

GO DEEPER

- **Helena drives at an average speed of 55 miles per hour. Does that mean she drove the same rate for the entire trip? Explain.** No; she may have driven at a slower rate some of the time and at a faster rate some of the time, but the average was 55 miles per hour.

Math Talk Follow this question by having students determine which formula to use if they were asked to find Helena's average speed, given her driving time and distance traveled.

ELL Strategy:
Identify Relationships

Have students write these problems and formulas on separate index cards.

Problem	Formula
You travel 80 miles at 20 miles per hour. How long are you traveling?	$d = r \times t$
You run at the rate of 7 yards per second for 12 seconds. How far do you run?	$r = d \div t$
You walk 4.5 miles in 1.5 hours. How fast are you walking?	$t = d \div r$

- Students match each problem card to the appropriate formula card. Have them explain their reasoning and identify what information in the problem is represented by the variable in the formula.

6.RP.A.3d Use ratio and rate reasoning to solve real-world and mathematical problems, e.g., by reasoning about tables of equivalent ratios, tape diagrams, double number line diagrams, or equations. Use ratio reasoning to convert measurement units; manipulate and transform units appropriately when multiplying or dividing quantities.

Name _____

Problem Solving • Distance, Rate, and Time Formulas

Common Core Ratios and Proportional Relationships—6.RP.A.3d
MATHEMATICAL PRACTICES
MP1, MP3, MP7

Essential Question How can you use the strategy *use a formula* to solve problems involving distance, rate, and time?

You can solve problems involving distance, rate, and time by using the formulas below. In each formula, *d* represents distance, *r* represents rate, and *t* represents time.

Distance, Rate, and Time Formulas		
To find distance, use	To find rate, use	To find time, use
$d = r \times t$	$r = d \div t$	$t = d \div r$

Unlock the Problem

Helena drives 220 miles to visit Niagara Falls. She drives at an average speed of 55 miles per hour. How long does the trip take?

Use the graphic organizer to help you solve the problem.

Read the Problem	**Solve the Problem**
What do I need to find? I need to find the __amount of time__ the trip takes.	• First write the formula for finding time. $t = d \div r$
What information do I need to use? I need to use the __distance__ Helena travels and the __rate__ of speed her car is moving.	• Next substitute the values for *d* and *r*. $t = $ __220__ mi $\div \dfrac{55 \text{ mi}}{1 \text{ hr}}$ • Rewrite the division as multiplication by the reciprocal of $\frac{55 \text{ mi}}{1 \text{ hr}}$. $t = \dfrac{220 \text{ mi}}{1} \times \dfrac{1 \text{ hr}}{55 \text{ mi}} = $ __4__ hr
How will I use the information? First I will choose the formula __$t = d \div r$__ because I need to find time. Next I will substitute for *d* and *r*. Then I will __divide__ to find the time.	**Math Talk** MATHEMATICAL PRACTICES ⑦ Look for Structure How do you know which formula to use?

So, the trip takes __4__ hours.

Possible answer: The value you are trying to find should be on one side of the equal sign by itself.

Reteach 6.5 ▲ RtI

Lesson 6.5
Reteach

Name _____

Problem Solving • Distance, Rate, and Time Formulas

Use a formula to solve the problem.

A bug crawls at a rate of 2 feet per minute. How long will it take the bug to crawl 25 feet?

Read the Problem	Solve the Problem
What do I need to find? I need to find the amount of time it will take the bug to crawl 25 feet	Write the appropriate formula. $t = d \div r$
What information do I need to use? I need to use the distance the bug crawls and the rate at which the bug crawls.	Substitute the values for *d* and *r*. $t = $ __25__ ft $\div \frac{2 \text{ ft}}{1 \text{ min}}$
How will I use the information? First I will choose the formula $t = d \div r$ because I need to find time. Next I will substitute __25 ft__ for *d* and __$\frac{2 \text{ ft}}{1 \text{ min}}$__ for *r*. Then I will __divide__ to find the time.	Rewrite the division as multiplication by the reciprocal. $t = \frac{25 \text{ ft}}{1} \times \frac{1 \text{ min}}{2 \text{ ft}} = $ __12.5__ min

1. A family drives for 3 hours at an average rate of 57 miles per hour. How far does the family travel?

__171 miles__

2. A train traveled 283.5 miles in 3.5 hours. What was the train's average rate of speed?

__81 miles per hour__

Chapter Resources
6-13
Reteach

Enrich 6.5 — Differentiated Instruction

Lesson 6.5
Enrich

Name _____

On Your Mark, Get Set, GO!!!!!

The car that travels farther wins. Name the car that wins each race.

Race #1 ____ Car B ____
- 30 mi per hr for 3 hr and 40 mi per hr for 2 hr — CAR A
- 35 mi per hr for 2 hr and 38 mi per hr for 3 hr — CAR B

Race #2 ____ Car A ____
- 54 mi per hr for 3 hr and 61 mi per hr for 3 hr — CAR A
- 74 mi per hr for 4 hr and 21 mi per hr for 2 hr — CAR B

Race #3 ____ Car A ____
- 46 mi per hr for 2 hr, 64 mi per hr for 1.5 hr, and 57 mi per hr for 3 hr — CAR A
- 51 mi per hr for 7 hr — CAR B

Race #4 ____ Car B ____
- 54 mi per hr for 2.5 hr and 44 mi per hr for 3 hr — CAR A
- 24 mi per hr for 3.5 hr and 84 mi per hr for 2.5 hr — CAR B

Race #5 ____ tie ____
- Started 6:30 A.M., finished 11:30 A.M. Rate 56 mi per hr. — CAR A
- Started 7:30 A.M., finished 11:30 A.M. Rate 70 mi per hr. — CAR B

Chapter Resources
6-14
Enrich

Try Another Problem

Santiago's class traveled to the Museum of Natural Science for a field trip. To reach the destination, the bus traveled at a rate of 65 miles per hour for 2 hours. What distance did Santiago's class travel?

Choose a formula.

$d = r \times t$ $r = d \div t$ $t = d \div r$

Use the graphic organizer below to help you solve the problem.

Read the Problem	Solve the Problem
What do I need to find? I need to find the distance traveled.	• Write the formula. $d = r \times t$
What information do I need to use? I need to use the rate of 65 miles per hour and the time of 2 hours.	• Substitute the values for r and t in the formula and multiply. $d = \frac{65 \text{ mi}}{1 \text{ hr}} \times \frac{2 \text{ hr}}{1} = 130$ mi
How will I use the information? First I will choose the formula $d = r \times t$ because I need to find the distance. Next I will substitute $\frac{65 \text{ mi}}{1 \text{ hr}}$ for r and 2 hr for t. Last, I will multiply to find the distance.	Possible answer: I know that the bus traveled 65 miles the first hour and 65 miles the second hour, or 65 + 65 = 130 miles in all.

 MATHEMATICAL PRACTICES ①

Evaluate How could you check your answer by solving the problem a different way?

So, Santiago's class traveled ____130____ miles.

1. **What if** the bus traveled at a rate of 55 miles per hour for 2.5 hours? How would the distance be affected?

   Possible answer: The distance would increase to 137.5 miles.

2. **MATHEMATICAL PRACTICE ⑦** Identify Relationships Describe how to find the rate if you are given the distance and time.

   Substitute values for d and t in the formula $r = d \div t$, and then divide the distance by the time to find the rate.

342

© Houghton Mifflin Harcourt Publishing Company • Image Credits: (t) ©John Zich/Stringer/Getty Images

Try Another Problem

Help students prepare to see different ways of asking for distance, rate, or time.

• **What does "how far" ask for?** distance
• **What does "how fast" ask for?** rate
• **What does "how long does it take" ask for?** time

After students complete the problem, elicit the following alternate method and generalization.

• **How far did the bus travel in the first hour? In the second hour?** 65 miles; 65 miles
• **How can you find the distance the bus traveled in those 2 hours?** Add: 65 + 65 = 130
• **Is your result from adding equal to your result from using the formula?** yes
• **In general, how can you check a distance found by using the formula?** Use the distance traveled each hour (or other unit of time). Add to find the total.

 You may suggest that students place completed Try Another Problem graphic organizer in their portfolios.

 Math Talk Elicit the fact from students that they can also check the problem by dividing 130 miles by either 65 miles per hour or 2 hours.

MP7 Look for and make use of structure.

• **What two operations appear in the three distance, rate, and time formulas? What is the relationship between those two operations?** multiplication and division; They are inverse operations.

Advanced Learners

🕐 Logical / Mathematical
Individual / Partners

• Have students solve the following problems that require converting units.

Malcolm drove for 12 minutes at the rate of 40 miles per hour and then 20 minutes at the rate of 30 miles per hour. How far did Malcolm drive? Convert minutes to hours and then use the distance formula. 12 min = $\frac{12}{60}$ hr = $\frac{1}{5}$ hr, 20 min = $\frac{20}{60}$ hr = $\frac{1}{3}$ hr

Distance at 40 mi per hr: $d = r \times t$; 40 × $\frac{1}{5}$ = 8 mi; Distance at 30 mi per hr: $d = r \times t$; 30 × $\frac{1}{3}$ = 10 mi; Total distance: 8 + 10 = 18 mi

Jill rode her bicycle 6 miles in 30 minutes and then 14 miles in 1 hour. What was her average rate? Find the total distance. 6 + 14 = 20 mi; Find the total time. 30 min + 1 hr = 1 hr 30 min = 1.5 hr; $r = d \div t$ = 20 ÷ 1.5 ≈ 13.3 Jill's average rate was approximately 13.3 mi per hr.

⚠ COMMON ERRORS

Error Students may choose an incorrect formula to solve the problem.

Example For Exercise 6 on page 343, students may choose the formula $d = r \times t$.

Springboard to Learning Remind students to look for key words in the problem such as "how long will it take" to help them determine what value they are being asked to find. In this case, "how long will it take" means they need to find the length of time.

③ EXPLAIN

Share and Show

The first problem connects to the learning model. Have students use the MathBoard to explain their thinking. For each exercise, have students identify the two given quantities and then identify the quantity they need to find.

Use the checked exercises for **Quick Check**. Remind students to show their work and answers on the MathBoard.

 Quick Check

If → a student misses the checked exercises

Then → **Differentiate Instruction with**
- Reteach 6.5
- Personal Math Trainer 6.RP.A.3d
- RtI Tier 1 Activity (online)

For Exercise 2, ask: **How many 5-minute segments are in 20 minutes?** 4

 For Exercise 6, ask: **What ratio do you need to find in order to solve the problem?** $\frac{3 \text{ miles}}{\blacksquare \text{ seconds}}$

THINK SMARTER

For Exercise 7, ask: **How many minutes does the cyclist need to ride 1 mile?** 4 mins **How many 4-minute segments are there in an hour?** 15

Name _____

Share and Show

Unlock the Problem

√ Choose the appropriate formula.
√ Include the unit in your answer.

1. Mariana runs at a rate of 180 meters per minute. How far does she run in 5 minutes?

   First, choose a formula.

   $$d = r \times t$$

   Next, substitute the values into the formula and solve.

   $$d = \frac{180 \text{ m}}{1 \text{ min}} \times 5 \text{ min} = 900 \text{ m}$$

   So, Mariana runs ___900 meters___ in 5 minutes.

2. **THINK SMARTER** What if Mariana runs for 20 minutes at the same speed? How many kilometers will she run?

   ___3.6 km___

☑ 3. A car traveled 130 miles in 2 hours. How fast did the car travel?

   ___65 mi per hr___

☑ 4. A subway car travels at a rate of 32 feet per second. How far does it travel in 16 seconds?

   ___512 ft___

5. A garden snail travels at a rate of 2.6 feet per minute. At this rate, how long will it take for the snail to travel 65 feet?

   ___25 min___

6. **GO DEEPER** A squirrel can run at a maximum speed of 12 miles per hour. At this rate, how many seconds will it take the squirrel to run 3 miles?

   ___900 seconds___

7. **THINK SMARTER** A cyclist rides 8 miles in 32 minutes. What is the speed of the cyclist in miles per hour?

   ___15 miles per hour___

© Houghton Mifflin Harcourt Publishing Company

WRITE ▸ Math ▸ **Show Your Work**

On Your Own

8. A pilot flies 441 kilometers in 31.5 minutes. What is the speed of the airplane?

14 km per min

9. **GO DEEPER** Chris spent half of his money on a pair of headphones. Then he spent half of his remaining money on CDs. Finally, he spent his remaining $12.75 on a book. How much money did Chris have to begin with?

_$51_

10. **THINK SMARTER** André and Yazmeen leave at the same time and travel 75 miles to a fair. André drives 11 miles in 12 minutes. Yazmeen drives 26 miles in 24 minutes. If they continue at the same rates, who will arrive at the fair first? Explain.

Yazmeen will arrive first. She travels 1.08 mi

per min while André travels 0.92 mi per min.

WRITE ▸Math
Show Your Work

11. **MATHEMATICAL PRACTICE ❸** Make Arguments Bonnie says that if she drives at an average rate of 40 miles per hour, it will take her about 2 hours to drive 20 miles across town. Does Bonnie's statement make sense? Explain.

No; if Bonnie travels 20 mi at an average rate of 40 mi

per hr, she will make it across town in half an hour.

Personal Math Trainer

12. **THINK SMARTER +** Claire says that if she runs at an average rate of 6 miles per hour, it will take her about 2 hours to run 18 miles. Do you agree or disagree with Claire? Use numbers and words to support your answer.

Disagree. Possible explanation: I used the formula

$t = d \div r$. _So,_ $t = 18 \text{ miles} \div \frac{6 \text{ miles}}{1 \text{ hour}}$. _I rewrote as a_

multiplication problem: $t = 18 \text{ miles} \times \frac{1 \text{ hour}}{6 \text{ miles}} = 3 \text{ hours}$.

It would take Claire 3 hours to run 18 miles.

344

© Houghton Mifflin Harcourt Publishing Company

DIFFERENTIATED INSTRUCTION INDEPENDENT ACTIVITIES

Differentiated Centers Kit

Activities
Rates

Students complete online purple Activity Card 16 by comparing rates of growth.

Literature
A Peek into a Tiny World

Students read about using a stage micrometer to make measurements of tiny creatures.

On Your Own

- **You need to find speed in Exercise 8. What unit of measure will you include in your answer?** km per min

Exercise 10 requires students to use higher-order thinking skills by analyzing two rates. Suggest that students start by finding the unit rate for each person.

Math on the Spot
Video Tutor

Use this video to help students model and solve this type of _Think Smarter_ problem.

 Math on the Spot videos are in the Interactive Student Edition and at _www.thinkcentral.com_.

MP3 Construct viable arguments and critique the reasoning of others. Have students justify their answers to Exercise 11 by using one of the formulas.

THINK SMARTER +
Personal Math Trainer

Be sure to assign this problem to students in the Personal Math Trainer. It features an animation to help them model and answer the problem. This item presents students with the opportunity to verify the reasoning of others. Students who answer the item correctly, but are unable to explain their answer, may not have a full understanding of how to solve a problem using the formula $t = d \div r$.

---

❺ EVALUATE Formative Assessment

Essential Question
Using the Language Objective

Reflect Have students review and rephrase examples from the lesson to answer the Essential Question.

How can you use the strategy _use a formula_ to solve problems involving distance, rate, and time? Use the appropriate formula, substitute the given values, and include the correct unit of measure in your answer.

Math Journal **WRITE** ▸Math

Describe the location of the variable _d_ in the formulas involving rate, time, and distance.

Practice and Homework

Use the Practice and Homework pages to provide students with more practice of the concepts and skills presented in this lesson. Students master their understanding as they complete practice items and then challenge their critical thinking skills with Problem Solving. Use the Write Math section to determine student's understanding of content for this lesson. Encourage students to use their Math Journals to record their answers.

Name _____

Problem Solving • Distance, Rate, and Time Formulas

COMMON CORE STANDARD—6.RP.A.3d
Understand ratio concepts and use ratio reasoning to solve problems.

Read each problem and solve.

1. A downhill skier is traveling at a rate of 0.5 mile per minute. How far will the skier travel in 18 minutes?

$d = r \times t$

$d = \dfrac{0.5 \text{ mi}}{1 \text{ min}} \times 18 \text{ min}$

$d = 9 \text{ miles}$

2. How long will it take a seal swimming at a speed of 8 miles per hour to travel 52 miles?

_____ 6.5 hr _____

3. A dragonfly traveled at a rate of 35 miles per hour for 2.5 hours. What distance did the dragonfly travel?

_____ 87.5 mi _____

4. A race car travels 1,212 kilometers in 4 hours. What is the car's rate of speed?

_____ 303 km per hr _____

5. Kim and Jay leave at the same time to travel 25 miles to the beach. Kim drives 9 miles in 12 minutes. Jay drives 10 miles in 15 minutes. If they both continue at the same rate, who will arrive at the beach first?

_____ Kim _____

6. **WRITE** ▸*Math* Describe the location of the variable d in the formulas involving rate, time, and distance.

Possible answer: In the formula for finding distance, the variable d is located by itself

on one side of the equal sign. In the formulas for finding rate and time, the variable d

is on the same side as, and is divided by one of the other variables.

Chapter 6   345

© Houghton Mifflin Harcourt Publishing Company

PROFESSIONAL DEVELOPMENT

Mathematical Practices in Your Classroom

CCSS.Math.Practice.MP6 Attend to precision.

Specifying units of measure is important for communicating precisely in mathematics. When manipulating units by using the distance, rate, and time formulas, students must be able to identify which units correspond to each measurement. They should also understand that units must be compatible. For example, if a distance is given in miles and a rate is given in feet per minute, the distance must be converted to feet or the rate must be converted to miles per minute in order to find the travel time.

Ask questions such as the following to help students recognize the importance of units in the problems in this lesson.

- **What is being measured if a quantity is given in units of feet per second? Explain.** A rate of speed because speed is measured in units of distance per unit of time.

- **A problem gives a distance in feet and a rate in feet per second. It asks for the time in seconds. How can you end up with seconds as the unit of your answer?** When you divide units of feet by units of feet per second, you can rewrite the division as multiplication by the reciprocal. Then you can divide the units of feet, which leaves only units of seconds.

- **How can you give an answer in inches if the problem gives a rate in feet per minute and a time in minutes?** Possible answer: Multiply the rate by the time to get a distance in feet. Then convert units of feet to units of inches by using a conversion factor.

1. Mark cycled 25 miles at a rate of 10 miles per hour. How long did it take Mark to cycle 25 miles?

_____ 2.5 hours _____

2. Joy ran 13 miles in $3\frac{1}{4}$ hours. What was her average rate?

_____ 4 miles per hour _____

Spiral Review (6.RP.A.3a, 6.RP.A.3c, 6.RP.A.3d)

3. Write two ratios that are equivalent to $\frac{9}{12}$.

Students' answers will vary. Possible

answer: $\frac{3}{4}$, $\frac{18}{24}$

4. In the Chang family's budget, 0.6% of the expenses are for internet service. What fraction of the family's expenses is for internet service? Write the fraction in simplest form.

$\frac{3}{500}$

5. How many meters are equivalent to 357 centimeters?

_____ 3.57 meters _____

6. What is the product of the two quantities shown below?

$$\frac{60\ mi}{1\ hr} \times 12\ hr$$

_____ 720 miles _____

© Houghton Mifflin Harcourt Publishing Company

**FOR MORE PRACTICE
GO TO THE
Personal Math Trainer**

Continue concepts and skills practice with Lesson Check. Use Spiral Review to engage students in previously taught concepts and to promote content retention. Common Core standards are correlated to each section.

Chapter 6
Review/Test

Summative Assessment

Use the **Chapter Review/Test** to assess students' progress in Chapter 6.

You may want to review with students the essential question for the chapter.

Chapter Essential Question

How can you use measurements to help you describe and compare objects?

Ask the following questions to focus students' thinking:

- **Why do you need to convert between units of measure?**
- **How can you use a ratio to convert units?**
- **How do you transform units to solve problems?**

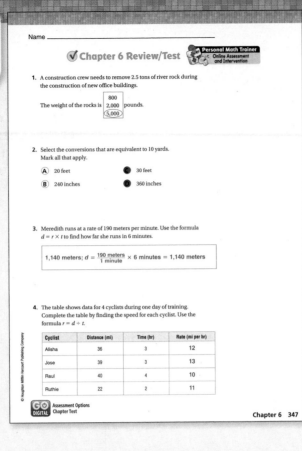

✓ Data-Driven Decision Making ▲ RtI   Chapter 6

Based on the results of the Chapter Review/Test use the following resources to review skills.

Item	Lesson	Standard	Content Focus	Personal Math Trainer	Intervene with
1, 7b, 9, 12, 15	6.3	6.RP.A.3d	Convert units of weight and mass.	6.RP.A.3d	**R—6.3**
2, 5, 7a, 7d, 8	6.1	6.RP.A.3d	Convert units of length.	6.RP.A.3d	**R—6.1**
3, 4, 16, 17	6.5	6.RP.A.3d	Solve a problem using the distance formula.	6.RP.A.3d	**R—6.5**
10, 11, 13, 18, 19, 20	6.4	6.RP.A.3d	Transform units to solve problems.	6.RP.A.3d	**R—6.4**
6, 7c, 14	6.2	6.RP.A.3d	Convert units of capacity.	6.RP.A.3d	**R—6.2**

Key: R—Reteach (in the *Chapter Resources*)

9. Write the mass measurements in order from least to greatest.

| 7.4 kilograms | 7.4 decigrams | 7.4 centigrams |

7.4 centigrams   7.4 decigrams   7.4 kilograms

10. An elephant's heart beats 28 times per minute. Complete the product to find how many times its heart beats in 30 minutes.

$$\boxed{28} \frac{\text{beats}}{\text{1 minute}} \times \boxed{30} \frac{\text{minutes}}{\text{1}} = \boxed{840} \text{ beats}$$

11. The length of a rectangular football field, including both end zones, is 120 yards. The area of the field is 57,600 square feet. For numbers 11a–11d, select True or False for each statement.

11a. The width of the field is 480 yards. ○ True ● False

11b. The length of the field is 360 feet. ● True ○ False

11c. The width of the field is 160 feet. ● True ○ False

11d. The area of the field is 6,400 square yards. ○ True ● False

12. Harry received a package for his birthday. The package weighed 357,000 centigrams. Select the conversions that are equivalent to 357,000 centigrams. Mark all that apply.

● 3.57 kilograms

● 357 dekagrams

● 3,570 grams

○ 3,570,000 decigrams

---

13. Mr. Martin wrote the following problem on the board.

> Juanita's car has a gas mileage of 21 miles per gallon. How many miles can Juanita travel on 7 gallons of gas?

Alex used the expression $\frac{21 \text{ miles}}{1 \text{ gallon}} \times \frac{1}{7 \text{ gallons}}$ to find the answer. Explain Alex's mistake.

Alex should have used $\frac{21 \text{ miles}}{1 \text{ gallon}} \times \frac{7 \text{ gallons}}{1}$.

14. Mr. Chen filled his son's wading pool with 20 gallons of water.

20 gallons is equivalent to [80 / 60 / 40] quarts.

15. Nadia has a can of vegetables with a mass of 411 grams. Write equivalent conversions in the correct boxes.

| 4.11 | 41.1 | 0.411 |

kilograms	hectograms	dekagrams
0.411	4.11	41.1

16. Steve is driving 440 miles to visit the Grand Canyon. He drives at an average rate of 55 miles per hour. Explain how you can find the amount of time it will take Steve to get to the Grand Canyon.

> Possible explanation: To find the amount of time it will take him, use the formula $t = d \div r$. $t = \frac{440 \text{ mi}}{1} \div \frac{55 \text{ mi}}{1 \text{ hr}}$, $t = 8$ hr.

---

17. Lucy walks one time around the lake. She walks for 1.5 hours at an average rate of 3 miles per hour. What is the distance, in miles, around the lake?

_____4.5_____ miles

18. The parking lot at a store has a width of 20 yards 2 feet and a length of 30 yards.

20 yards 2 feet
30 yards

Part A

Derrick says that the width could also be written as 22 feet. Explain whether you agree or disagree with Derrick.

> I disagree. Possible explanation: The width is 20 yards + 2 feet, and since there are 3 feet in one yard, the width would be (20 yards × 3 feet per yard) + 2 feet = 62 feet.

Part B

The cost to repave the parking lot is $2 per square foot. Explain how much it would cost to repave the parking lot.

> Possible explanation: Since the cost is per square foot, find the area of the lot. First, convert the length and width to feet: 20 yd 2 ft = 62 ft and 30 yd = 90 ft. Then, find the area: 62 ft × 90 ft = 5,580 ft². Since the cost is $2 per square foot, multiply 5,580 by 2: 5,580 × 2 = 11,160. The cost is $11,160.

---

19. **THINK SMARTER** | **Personal Math Trainer** Jake is using a horse trailer to take his horses to his new ranch.

Part A

Complete the table by finding the weight, in pounds, of Jake's horse trailer and each horse.

	Weight (T)	Weight (lb)
Horse	0.5	1,000
Trailer	1.25	2,500

Part B

Jake's truck can tow a maximum weight of 5,000 pounds. What is the maximum number of horses he can take in his trailer at one time without going over the maximum weight his truck can tow? Use numbers and words to support your answer.

> Jake can take a maximum of 2 horses in his trailer at one time. Possible explanation: The weight of 2 horses and the trailer would be 2 × 1,000 + 2,500 = 4,500. 4,500 pounds is less than 5,000 pounds. The weight of 3 horses and the trailer would be 3 × 1,000 + 2,500 = 5,500. 5,500 pounds is greater than 5,000 pounds.

20. A rectangular room measures 13 feet by 132 inches. Tonya said the area of the room is 1,716 square feet. Explain her mistake, then find the area in square feet.

> Possible explanation: Tanya multiplied 13 and 132. She should have converted 132 inches to 11 feet before she found the area. The correct area is 13 feet × 11 feet = 143 square feet.

Performance Assessment Task
Chapter 6

See *Chapter Resources* for a Performance Task that assesses students' understanding of the content of this chapter.

For each task, you will find sample student work for each of the response levels in the task scoring rubric.

Critical Area Performance Assessment Tasks
Chapters 4–6

See the *Chapter Resources* for a Performance Task that assesses students' understanding of the content of this Critical Area.

Portfolio Performance Assessment Tasks may be used for portfolios.

Be sure to assign students Exercise 19 in the Personal Math Trainer. It features an animation or video to help students model and solve the problem.

Summative Assessment

Use the **Chapter Test** to assess students' progress in Chapter 6.

Chapter Tests are provided in Common Core assessment formats in the *Chapter Resources*.

Personal Math Trainer

Name _____ Chapter 6 Test Page 1

1. Fran's snowmobile weighs 0.8 ton. The weight of the

snowmobile is (1,600) pounds.
   - 800
   - **1,600**
   - 2,500

2. Select the conversions that are equivalent to 25 yards. Mark all that apply.

   (A) 50 feet   ● 75 feet

   ● 900 inches   (D) 1000 inches

3. A subway car travels at a rate of 32 meters per second. How far does it travel in 16 seconds? Use $d = r \times t$.

   512 meters; $\frac{32 \text{ meters}}{1 \text{ second}} \times \frac{16 \text{ seconds}}{1} = 512$ meters

4. The table shows data from 4 runners during a training session.

   Complete the table by finding the rate for each cyclist. Use the formula $r = d \div t$.

Runner	Distance (kilometers)	Time (hours)	Rate (km per hour)
Molly	3.0	3	1
Jesse	3.2	2	1.6
Nathan	4.0	4	1
Susie	2.2	2	1.1

   GO ON

Name _____ Chapter 6 Test Page 2

5. For numbers 5a–5c, choose <, >, or =.

   5a. 7,000 meters [<, >, =] 7 kilometers

   5b. 31.6 grams [<, >, =] 316 centigrams

   5c. 4 liters [<, >, =] 400 milliliters

6. For Sunday brunch, Alisha is making a recipe that requires 8 cups of milk. She has 3 quarts of milk. Does she have enough for the recipe? Explain your answer using numbers and words.

   Yes, Alisha has enough milk. There are 4 cups in 1 quart. She has 3 × 4 = 12 cups, and 12 is greater than 8.

7. For numbers 7a–7d, choose <, >, or =.

   7a. 4 kilometers [<, >, =] 5000 meters   7c. 10 quarts [<, >, =] 2.5 gallons

   7b. 2.5 tons [<, >, =] 4000 pounds   7d. 60 yards [<, >, =] 600 inches

8. The distance from Joshua's house to the mall is 3.5 miles. The distance from Meg's house to the mall is 19,000 feet. Who lives closer to the mall, Joshua or Meg? Use numbers and words to support your answer.

   Joshua lives closer to the mall. I converted 3.5 miles to 18,480 feet and then compared this distance to 19,000 feet. 18,480 feet is the shorter distance.

   GO ON

✓ Data-Driven Decision Making ▲ RtI

Based on the results of the Chapter Review/Test use the following resources to review skills.

Item	Lesson	Standard	Content Focus	Personal Math Trainer	Intervene with
1, 7b, 9, 12, 15	6.3	6.RP.A.3d	Convert units of weight and mass.	6.RP.A.3d	**R**—6.3
2, 5, 7a, 7d, 8	6.1	6.RP.A.3d	Convert units of length.	6.RP.A.3d	**R**—6.1
3, 4, 16, 17	6.5	6.RP.A.3d	Solve a problem using the distance formula.	6.RP.A.3d	**R**—6.5
10, 11, 13, 18, 19, 20	6.4	6.RP.A.3d	Transform units to solve problems.	6.RP.A.3d	**R**—6.4
6, 7c, 14	6.2	6.RP.A.3d	Convert units of capacity.	6.RP.A.3d	**R**—6.2

Key: R—Reteach (in the *Chapter Resources*)

9. Write the mass measurements in order from least to greatest.

| 3.2 kilograms | 3.2 decigrams | 3.2 centigrams |

3.2 centigrams, 3.2 decigrams, 3.2 kilograms

10. A dripping faucet leaks 1.8 ounces per minute. Complete the product to find how many ounces it leaks in half an hour.

$\dfrac{1.8 \text{ ounces}}{1 \text{ minute}} \times \dfrac{30 \text{ minutes}}{1} =$ __54__ ounces

11. The rectangular rug in Marcia's living room measures 15 feet by 120 inches. For numbers 11a–11d, select True or False for each statement.

11a. The area of the rug is 150 square feet.   ● True   ○ False

11b. The length of the rug is 150 inches.   ○ True   ● False

11c. The width of the rug is 10 feet.   ● True   ○ False

11d. The area of the rug is 21,600 square inches.   ● True   ○ False

12. Henrietta bought a box of books that weighs 560,000 centigrams.

Select the measurements that are equivalent to 560,000 centigrams. Mark all that apply.

Ⓐ 5,600,000 decigrams

Ⓑ 5.60 kilograms

Ⓒ 560 dekagrams

Ⓓ 5,600 grams

GO ON

13. Ms. Woodson wrote the problem on the board.

Mark's car has a gas mileage of 30 miles per gallon. How many miles can Mark travel on 13 gallons of gas?

Pamela used $\dfrac{30 \text{ miles}}{1 \text{ gallon}} \times \dfrac{1}{13 \text{ gallons}}$ to find the answer. Explain Pamela's mistake.

> Pamela should have multiplied $\dfrac{30 \text{ miles}}{1 \text{ gallon}} \times 13$ gallons to get 390 miles.

14. Becky's water bottle could hold 0.9 liter of water.

0.9 liter is equivalent to [0.9 / 0.09 / **0.0009**] kiloliter.

15. The mass of a standard hockey puck must be at least 156 grams. Write equivalent conversions in the correct boxes.

| 15,600 | 1.56 | 0.156 |

kilograms	centigrams	hectograms
0.156	15,600	1.56

16. Sherry is driving 390 miles to visit the Gateway Arch in St. Louis. She drives at an average rate of 65 miles per hour. Explain how you can find the amount of time it will take Sherry to get to the Arch.

> Possible explanation: To find the amount of time it will take her, use the formula $t = d \div r$: $t = \dfrac{390 \text{ mi}}{1} \div \dfrac{65 \text{ mi}}{1 \text{ hr}}$; $t = 6$ hr.

17. Lydia takes a brisk walk around a pond. She walks 1.25 hours at an average speed of 3 miles per hour. What is the distance around the pond?

__3.75__ miles

GO ON

18. A rectangular table cloth has a width of 3 yards 1 foot and a length of 4 yards.

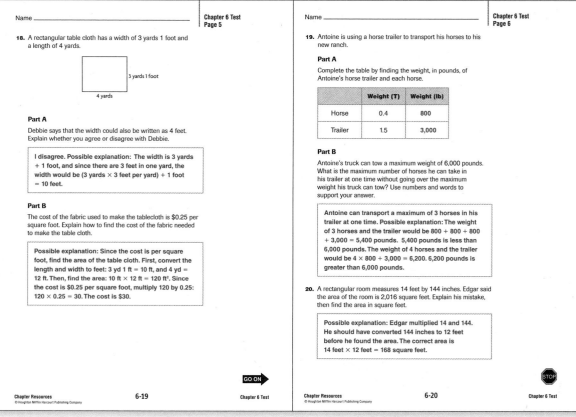

3 yards 1 foot

4 yards

Part A

Debbie says that the width could also be written as 4 feet. Explain whether you agree or disagree with Debbie.

> I disagree. Possible explanation: The width is 3 yards + 1 foot, and since there are 3 feet in one yard, the width would be (3 yards × 3 feet per yard) + 1 foot = 10 feet.

Part B

The cost of the fabric used to make the tablecloth is $0.25 per square foot. Explain how to find the cost of the fabric needed to make the table cloth.

> Possible explanation: Since the cost is per square foot, find the area of the table cloth. First, convert the length and width to feet: 3 yd 1 ft = 10 ft, and 4 yd = 12 ft. Then, find the area: 10 ft × 12 ft = 120 ft². Since the cost is $0.25 per square foot, multiply 120 by 0.25: 120 × 0.25 = 30. The cost is $30.

GO ON

19. Antoine is using a horse trailer to transport his horses to his new ranch.

Part A

Complete the table by finding the weight, in pounds, of Antoine's horse trailer and each horse.

	Weight (T)	Weight (lb)
Horse	0.4	800
Trailer	1.5	3,000

Part B

Antoine's truck can tow a maximum weight of 6,000 pounds. What is the maximum number of horses he can take in his trailer at one time without going over the maximum weight his truck can tow? Use numbers and words to support your answer.

> Antoine can transport a maximum of 3 horses in his trailer at one time. Possible explanation: The weight of 3 horses and the trailer would be 800 + 800 + 800 + 3,000 = 5,400 pounds. 5,400 pounds is less than 6,000 pounds. The weight of 4 horses and the trailer would be 4 × 800 + 3,000 = 6,200. 6,200 pounds is greater than 6,000 pounds.

20. A rectangular room measures 14 feet by 144 inches. Edgar said the area of the room is 2,016 square feet. Explain his mistake, then find the area in square feet.

> Possible explanation: Edgar multiplied 14 and 144. He should have converted 144 inches to 12 feet before he found the area. The correct area is 14 feet × 12 feet = 168 square feet.

STOP

Portfolio

Portfolio Suggestions

The portfolio represents the growth, talents, achievements, and reflections of the mathematics learner. Students might spend a short time selecting work samples for their portfolios.

You may want to have students respond to the following questions:

- What new understanding of math have I developed in the past several weeks?
- What growth in understanding or skills can I see in my work?
- What can I do to improve my understanding of math ideas?
- What would I like to learn more about?

For information about how to organize, share, and evaluate portfolios, see the *Chapter Resources.*

Chapter 6 Test